The LUMIE TREE

612   BOULTER'S LOCK. — MAIDENHEAD — LL.

Stanley Woolf remembers Maidenhead

The LUMIE TREE

Town and Thames in the '20s —
a romance

BARRACUDA BOOKS LIMITED
BUCKINGHAM, ENGLAND
MCMLXXXVIII

TYPESET BY
QUILL AUTOGRAPHICS LIMITED

PRINTED BY
M. & A. THOMSON LITHO LTD

AND BOUND BY
CAMELOT PRESS PLC

ISBN 0 86023 296 4

Table of Contents

Dedication

For Dorothy

Mooghie — sweet Muriel Campbell, the doctor's daughter from Mariposa in Taplow.

1

A View from the Bridge

I quit the train at Taplow. Emotionally over-charged, I could no longer bear the briskness of railway rhythm. What I really needed was to bum along at my own pace and dream of the delights I had just left behind me.

At Maidenhead Bridge, stretching my arms along the parapet, already quite hot from the sun, the notion struck me how love and Mooghie had wrought within me a most startling revelation of what I truly felt for my native town. My Maidenhead - Terre Paradis! I lowered my head and prayed that it would never change, would remain forever as it was at this moment: a Heaven that we all took for granted in the grossest fashion, gentle and simple alike.

At my back I felt the ever-increasing pressure and volume of traffic, as it slowed to negotiate the steeply cambered road over the Bridge. Before me the river wound away by the islands to Boulters Lock. At Wilders' and Andrews' rafts, the punts drifted peacefully at their moorings in fan-shaped groups, lightly riding the clappiting currents. The sun's heat fell like an arm across my shoulders, though morning shadows were still long and skinny. From Skindles' dewy lawn a man was angling patiently, giving a twitch now and then to his line. I could hear the sharp whirr of his reel above the noise of the traffic. From the terrace to where he stood, he had left his foot-prints in the dew. The day of the cabin-cruiser had not yet come. There was peace upon the waters. Long, narrow launches with scalloped or fringed awnings glided beneath the Bridge, with a few little motor-boats puttering up to Boulters or down to Bray. In punts and skiffs men still sported straw boaters. Up by the islands a handsome white house-boat might have been painted that morning by Stanley Spencer himself.

The boats had pretty and exotic names....*Myosotis, Rouge et Noir, Farfalla.* Rather more elderly craft recalled a time when upper-class women had briefly adopted a geisha-look in their appearance: tiny bow lips, oblique slant to their outer eye-corners, a hobbly, cute way of ambling. *Onana San, Pitty-sing, Mikado*...I had known them as long as I had known that a river was a river. Most of my life I had enjoyed the delicious misery of gramophones softly braying in the summer beneath weeping willows. At dusk, with a melon-coloured moon rising and a warm breeze stirring the leaves, it was all unbearably lovely. At the time of which I write it was *Blue Skies, The Birth of the Blues* and, sometimes less elegiacally, *Piccolo Pete* or *So Is Your Old Lady.*

Suddenly my angler got a bite. A writhing silver arc leapt from the water, scattering a rainbow of prismatic drops. I cursed the fellow as he unhooked his catch then chucked it callously in the basket. For a split second my bliss faltered.

Now the sun had climbed. Shadows had shortened. The hither woodland slopes had changed from warm purple to golden-green. I turned about to survey the down-stream landscape. Away-drifting haze was steadily unveiling Brunel's miraculous brick archway. Augustly, nonchalantly, it took its giant stride across the wide river, whilst a County-Tank steamed across it, shrilling its whistle to let Maidenhead know that it was coming, trailing its pale plume of vapour. It was superb....the longest brick span in the world and subject of one of Turner's finest canvases; speed, rain and steam; bricks and mortar transmuted into a fairy sky-way.

At the bank the breeze scarcely fluttered the rushes. Soon it would be a real scorcher, a fine start for our holiday. I damned that holiday, feeling mean for doing so, but last night with its totally unexpected pleasures and promises still held me in a state of intoxication.

Between the branches in the middle-distance could be descried the tall Victorian houses of Gaiety Row, with their balconies and creepers.

When we were little kids and Mrs Melbury took us for walks by the river, I once asked her curiously why she almost invariably brought us in this particular direction. It had always puzzled me, the way she convulsively directed her eyes from window to window of these dwellings with a look in them of a malicious robin.

'It's them toffs,' she muttered in reply. 'That's where they keeps their naughty lidies — in AH-REEMS!'

'Naughty?' I queried. 'Why are they naughty — and how?'

Mrs Melbury bent upon me a narrow, uncertain glance: the kind adults of low personality-power bend upon bright, precocious kids.

The punts drifted peacefully at their moorings.

'Never you mind,' she miffed, taking refuge in convenient adulthood. 'Never you — 'ere, where you orf to?' She broke off in dismay. Little Tony was out of his go-cart and halfway up the nearest drive-way, performing a stupid little jig, which melted Pa's bowels with tenderness, and caused Victor and me to regret his being as yet too titchy to thump.

' 'ere, you come aht o' that!' shrilled Mrs Melbury. 'You little bug — beggar, you! Come aht or I'll 'ave yer traysers dayn! — Ow, moi Gawd!'

Now Tony was streaking for the sanctuary of his cart, followed from the gate by an elegant Delage coupé, driven by an ageing but still dashing military type in a grey bowler hat and monocle, beside whom lounged a splendid young female in grey-striped lavender silk, who peered indolently into the bright sunlight from a dear little veiled toque, with her black pansy eyes. As though from a sleepy excess of wellbeing, they smiled down at us in passing. I hoped to God that they hadn't taken Mrs Melbury for our mother.

'Trollope! Filth!' muttered Mrs Melbury viciously. 'Sellin' 'er body to the highest bidder: Floggin', tha's what she wants. From the cart's tile!'

'I like her,' declared Victor. 'I think she liked me too.'

'Garn!' growled our char-cum-nurse-maid. 'They thought we was orl crap. You an' me an' all!'

I regarded her with pitiless, unconcealed criticism, from her fusty black stockings to her hideous yellow straw hat; from her buttoned boots to her bilious complexion and acid-green eyes. For me she had ceased to be a woman at all. She looked more like a disgusting urchin in 'drag'.

Then and there, I decided never again to come spying with our dreadful Melbury upon the putative misdemeanours of the upper classes. Indeed, from that moment commenced my love affair with the rich and the great: necessarily one-sided, remote and vicarious, but a genuine and quite passionate affair for all that. From Gaiety Row my spirit took flight and soared off towards Cliveden and Taplow Court.

Now, from the Bridge, I wandered on up Bridge Road past the Moor, fingering the hoops of the dainty railings that had so captured my fancy as a small child. One of the slighter triumphs of Victorian craftsmen, they stretched from beyond Salters Almshouses and George Herring's Haven Of Rest nearly as far as Moor Bridge, enclosing a well-mown grass plot, planted with small dark-leaved trees. With that odd morbidity that sometimes visits children, I had often thought how nice it might be to have one's own grave protected by such an exquisite enclosure. An incurable fetishist, I never neglected to pass those delicately wrought hoops between my fingers, both going to and coming from the river. Their sole disadvantage, in my own view, lay in their passing proximity to the pious Mr Herring's ashes. These reposed beneath the ornamental sundial before the entrance to his Haven. I felt a rooted objection to these relics. They were weird, unseemly. Returning from riverside friends after dark, I would dodge across Bridge Road to avoid passing close to this horological sepulchre. Squeamish I was not. I had seen drowned corpses fished from the sweet Thames without batting an eyelid, not to mention others who, to judge from the agonies attending their

Dodging across Bridge Road was not too much of a hazard in the mid-'20s, (Bridge House on the left).

recoveries, might better have drowned outright and have done with it. These were routine misfortunes, mere holiday hazards, disasters that failed to tickle any morbid streak in me. But to leave orders to inter one's ashes, and to mark the spot where decent folk passed by, and aged inmates of his charity reposed and sunned their honourable rheumatisms....It was a coarse outrage: a disgusting lapse from good taste — albeit a final one. Had he been able to see, in a vision of the future, his house by the Bridge become the summer headquarters of the famous Murrays' Club from London's West End....a night club, what an admonition to giddy, irreligious revellers might his ashes have proved, placed in the very middle of the lawn, surmounting instead of underlying the sun-dial. What a momento mori! What a mummy at the feasting!

Reluctantly my fingers withdrew themselves from those dark green railings; warm to the touch, sensuously curvaceous. Across the Moor I descried three gipsy waggons surrounded by a mass of howling kids. Closer at hand a strappingly nubile girl was carrying two brimming buckets of water. To the swaying of her hips and breasts, silvery water dimpled and splashed around her bare and sinewy toes. She set me off. Instantly my heart tattooed. The emotional treasure, hoarded all that morning so jealously, a priceless store, was no longer to be contained. Breathless as I was, I took to my heels, nor paused until I drew level with Bridge Street Picture Palace. Full circle I had come since yesterday afternoon; for here, emerging from Fritz Lang's *Metropolis*, I had run into Muriel and her mother and been invited to tea out at Cygnet Green for the first time. My cup ran over with a resounding slosh because Muriel, in the few short weeks of the holiday, had transformed herself, as if by some magic potion, from a pretty thing with puppy-fat, into a smashing beauty with honey-blonde hair piled unfashionably but ravishingly high upon her head, a quite theatrical touch of make-up, and des petites poires comme ca! The soigné pulchritude of her mother just had to be seen to be believed. I saw. I believed.

2

High Street Redolence

I well recall the morning Mrs Melbury announced, by truly outrageous misconduct, that she 'drank!'

Pa, his breakfast digesting nicely, a day's leave ahead of him, read his *Daily Mail*, toasted his toes while cosily listening to his newest gramophone record. He believed in multiplying his pleasures, did Pa. The record was of Debussy's *L'apres Midi D'un Faun*. I thought it lovely, but Ma sneered disparagement of the Master's delicious impressionism. Outdoors, red leaves and gold, as if obedient to the subtly emergent rhythms, drifted gently by the French doors. Even my little brothers were guiltily quiet in a corner, forming anatomical ruderies out of plasticine. But for their occasional giggles, it was as peaceful a scene as one might have wished.

Without warning, as though blown in by an exploding bomb, Mrs Melbury, a hideous smear of black lead war-painting her contorted face, burst in upon us, snatched *L'apres Midi* from the turntable, and sent it crashing to the hearth, where it broke into a thousand pieces. She then staggered back and, with a loud cry of 'BLOODY-RAH!', immediately went out cold on the hearth-rug.

Ma, of course, was for summary dismissal, without a character reference. Pa, the very soul of compassion, except where his eldest son was concerned, was melted by the woman's maudlin contrition. Her daughter, Ethel ('Ah Athel') an usherette at Bridge Street Picture Palace, had either fallen or been pushed into the family way by a boatman from Wilder's, and promptly deserted. A recalcitrant kitchen-stove and raging tooth-ache on top of Ethel's fall from virtue, had been almost the back-breaking straw. It was old Debussy who

15

finally did it. Mrs Melbury had repaired straightaway to the cellar shelf where Pa was stocking up cheer for the Christmas festivities. Half a dozen gargantuan swigs on a nearly empty stomach 'had done her' business for her. Ma's objections were pitiable to behold; yet Pa's decision to overlook what he, with cheerful euphemism, called our char's little lapse, was adamantine. He liked his own glass far too well to want in sympathy towards a similar weakness in another. Moreover, the humours of alcohol were ever quick to tickle his funny-bone.

Pa did a deal with our friends the Spindlers at the opposite side of the Avenue. Mrs Melbury was reprieved, but only upon the condition that she was to be shared for the rough work by the two families, while their maid, Rose, took over the more genteel slavery, such as taking us for walks when she promenaded their daughter, Renee.

Riverside walks with a woman possessing Mrs Melbury's swallow might prove hazardous, Pa opined, for the survival of his offspring. In the jargon of our times, counter-productive.

When Muriel came into my life, I was just eight years old. Still seedy from an operation at Dunkel's Hospital for sick children, I stood by the blazing playroom fire, more than a little un-nerved by the cheery hell of play-time. Pearly mist pressed close against the French doors, and a robin trilled out of it, because a winter sun was about to break through.

I was, I suppose, suffering post-hospital insecurity. Mr Dunkels continued as an unobtrusive father-figure; Matron as a formidable tower of strength against all evil, and my favourite nurse Barnabus I currently cherished in the role of heroine in bedtime fantasies: rescuing her to the strains of wildly exciting music from fates worse than death.

Ernest Dunkels, mentioned by Mr Tom Middleton in his magnificent *Book of Maidenhead*, as a 'quiet benefactor', was all that and more. His lovely house, Woodhurst, in Ray Mead Road, he threw open as a hospital for children in the first World War, and there were not wanting uncharitable allusions in certain envious quarters to the country of his origin, nor

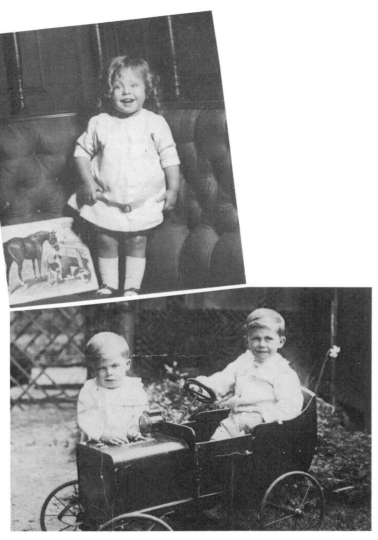

*At two years old, I looked upon the Gordon Road Laundry
fire, and a year or two later, got my first taste of motoring,
with brother Victor.*

17

snide remarks and shabby misconstructions upon his many kindnesses in several other directions. I actually heard one reverend gentleman observe that, in his opinion, Mr Dunkels was actuated, not so much by Christian charity, as a desire to ingratiate himself with his new compatriots. This was at a tea-fight given by a fungoid old lady in his parish. Perhaps a cup or two too many had given the lie to the curatish jest about tea and inebriation. I never cared for parsons much after that, and Pa's anti-clericalism further set me on the royal road to hell-fire.

Dunkel's photograph in Mr Middleton's admirable book shows a younger man than his small patients knew. He was good-looking and dark-haired and, on those occasions when, on a visit, he moved from bed to bed with a bar of extremely dark chocolate for each child sufficiently recovered to stomach it, his hair was streaked with grey, as was the thick moustache he had allowed to grow. Sixty years on I see him as clearly as if it were yesterday, and hear the slight stammer of his broken English. He was painfully bashful with us all. As he stood regarding one kindly from the foot of one's cot, an imperishable belief in his strength and utter dependability surrounded him. I shall never forget the wonderful wide windows of that cosy ward, with the strings of barges drifting in the misty light past the Islands, the enormous weeping willow of his front garden, and the staff all crisp and tarted up for his visit.

At that time, things at home were going far from smoothly. Pa, emaciated and battle-scarred, (he had a bayonet-wound across the back of his left hand, which was the pride and joy of our silly young lives), from fighting the Bolsheviki in Holy Mother Russia, was finding it tough settling down to the diurnal hum-drum of hairdressing. The popsy he was carrying on with, who lived in a dear little gothic-looking flint house on the Thicket, was French and piquantly pretty. Ma was driven to distraction by it all, and oft in the stilly night the two direful words 'That Woman' could he heard shrilling loudly and unmusically up the corridor. The domestic atmosphere became strongly flavoured with brimstone. Small wonder then that the security of Mr Dunkel's haven — so delectably different to that of the phantasmal Mr Herring — called me back with so enticing, so seductive a voice.

I had one more year to go at Queen Anne House before going on to the County Boys School in Shoppenhangers Road. I fancied myself quite a bit. So, when Miss Mayne came over with a new kid in pink gingham in tow, and gave her into my keeping, I came over all cocky and superior despite my lowness of spirits. It seemed she had been ill for some time and must not be treated roughly.

'So you will look after her, won't you, dear child? Take her round and introduce her to the other children. Let her stand in front of the fire for a moment or two, though. She has just come to the station.'

'Alright,' I said, more grudgingly than was necessary in the circumstances. 'I'll see she comes to no harm.'

Miss Bridger joined us, clasped her hands in one of her customary ecstasies and shrilled: 'Oh, Miss Mayne! Call them not Angles, but call them rather Angels! Aren't they utter darlings?'

I looked at my new protegé, noting that she was no happier than I at Miss Bridger's hysterical rhapsodising. We looked at each other, grinning shyly, exchanging blushes. I wanted to maim the stupid woman, but Muriel's pretty face expressed nothing but pity for a tame loony. I imagined that, if she were not such a well-mannered child, she might have placed one fore-finger at her temple and given it a twisted screw, to indicate her opinion of Miss Bridger's mental capacities. Her well-meant, spinsterish outburst of admiration did in fact lead us into being nick-named The Heavenly Twins. We both had blonde hair and sky-blue eyes, and perhaps physically merited her Gregorian hyperbole though, from thenceforth, we looked upon Miss Bridger with feelings far from angelic.

Some of the other kids showed a tendency to gather round us; to get a 'squint' at the new kid but Muriel was no more welcoming than I was. Nicer, yes, but equally discouraging.

'I shall be quite alright with Hubert,' she smiled shyly and they drifted away. There was something very determined in her gentle dismissal. The playroom fire had grown much too hot. I noticed that Muriel had gone rather pale, and drew her over towards the French-doors. The robin, perched upon a watering-can, sang with wide open beak right into our faces. The sun was well through, and the high-walled garden was a-glitter with frost. One of the espaliered apples still hung with bright red fruit like lanterns.

'Isn't it all lovely?' she said in a soft, low voice.

'What, the old winter sunshine and that?' I said with an air of exaggerated disparagement. 'I s'pose they're alright!'

The colour was returning to her cheeks. 'What's been the trouble with you, then?' I asked her.

'Slight inflammation of the lungs,' she replied. 'Nothing very much, but Daddy was worried about me. He's a doctor, you see. They always worry most about their sick families, don't they?'

'No doubt of that,' I said from the deep well of my life's experience.

'What has been wrong with you, Hubert dear?'

Hubert, dear! I must, I felt, put her in her place. I glanced foxily around me. Nobody seemed to have noticed her small endearment. I gave her incredible prettiness the once-over — a twice-over more accurately. I felt a subtle menace, a charm; there was mockery in her sea-blue eyes, in the arch of her golden brows. The corners of her eye-lids tilted slightly, almost orientally. Later on I was to liken them to magnolia petals in the jejeune verse, addressed to her during boring old maths, in the fourth form at County Boys. But at present, I was a village idiot in the spell of her enchantment. I must give her a bit of a shock, teach her where she got off, so to speak. With slit eyes I hissed:

'I've had a most terrible operation at Dunkel's. Nearly drew my curtains for me. Ever had an operation?'

'Oh, no — never!'

'Then don't. Before Dr Wilson dripped chloroform on that mask thing I saw terrible little knives and a saw and a wopping great brace and bit. Then—'

'Oh, please don't — it's too awful! Poor darling Hubert! Did it hurt much afterwards?'

'Did it hurt! When the stitches came out, I dam' nearly raised the roof. Matron's bonnet fell off. There were bent up scissors in glasses of coloured liquid. I wouldn't want to go through that again! Cor!'

'But it's better now? It doesn't hurt any more?'

I fired off my self-protective shocker,

'Only when I pee it itches like fun,' I said. 'And I've got a scar just like a Christmas tree just over my tiddler!'

I drew back apace, awaiting the shriek of maidenly outrage. Alas, it was no go. Her expression of sympathy deepened. Her lovely eyes misted with pity. Her lower lip drooped like a rose-petal opening.

'Where does your father do his doctoring?' I demanded with crude schoolboy bluntness. She flushed a little. 'Daddy practices out at Cygnet Green' she replied. 'I'm a train-child. That's why I was so late. I missed the first train, so mummy brought me in.'

'A train-kid! Crikey, that's jammy for you! You'll be having your dinner over at the big school. Gosh, it smells scrummy. Lucky old you! It's cold beef for us at home today and cold, slimey old apple tart. I've always wanted school dinner ever since I first came here!'

'Oh, poor you. Look — '

She was interrupted by Miss Mayne's strenuous concerto on the bell. Silence fell; there was a squeaky shuffle of plimsolls towards the play-room door. I trotted upstairs in the wake of my new girl-friend and was instantly ravished by her knickers, though knickers, to speak with accuracy, they most certainly were not. Short, tight little drawers, that's what they were, made of the same material as her gingham frock. It was the coup de foudre; nearly, indeed the coup de grace! I was out middle-stump: completely gimswiggled! Most of the Queen Anne girls wore indigo Winceyette horrors, speckled an acid-green where the flat-iron hit the seams. Many tucked their hankies and Sharp's Kreemy Toffee under the elastic. Renee did, for one. Now, totally captivated by Muriel's elfin undergarments, I followed in a condition of dizzy bewitchment. My depressing malaise had taken itself off. I was better.

Cold meat and mealy potatoes were indeed our lot, flavoured by the unappetising reek of washing wafted from Mrs Simpole's labours out in the wash-house. Spotted-dick followed, with a sudsy taste, suggestive of its having been plunged into the copper with our pants and socks.

But when I entered the side door of the red brick, pinnacled, preposterous folly that was Queen Anne House, who should be waiting for me in the mousey cloakroom but Muriel, with her school-dinner mince-pie neatly folded in a pink hanky.

'It's for you,' she whispered shyly. 'Some school-dinner. I didn't want it — really and truly.'

'Coo, thanks!' I exclaimed, concealing a sudden passion of gratitude.

'If you like you may keep the hanky too.' She blushed more deeply yet.

'Thanks,' I said, emotions showing through at last. 'Thanks! You're a brick, Muriel — a real brick!'

A quick smile lit up her face. 'What a lovely thing to say to me, Hubert, dear. So that is what ballet-class is doing for me. Thanks ever so much!'

'I — I didn't mean — '

'I know you didn't, silly. Let's hope the pie doesn't turn out to be one. What have you got next lesson?'

'English with old Dicky. She hates me like billy-o.'

'Nonsense, Hubert dear, nobody in their right senses could hate you. You're much too sweet.'

So saying, she gave me a cool little kiss on the cheek, turned and rushed upstairs two at a time, developing her fantastic little drawers alarmingly and leaving me in a state of juvenile fever.

At the time of Ethel's shame and her mother's débacle I was well over six. I spent three whole days and a half of each week at Queen Anne, and was thus able to enjoy the bliss of walks with Rose and the kids and Renee on Thursday afternoons, Fridays and Saturday.

Rose was enormous fun. She was a big-boned, flaxen Wessex girl from Avebury, full of what she called 'larks', and merrily zestful for anything that was going, however simple — whether it was a staid walk in the country, a picnic on the Thicket or just shop-window-gazing in our cosy Victorian town.

Friday we paid the tradesmen's books: compact little mini-ledgers with an oval aperture cut out of their front covers, enclosing one's name and decorated in the case of our butcher, Mr Fletcher, with a marvellous golden pig.

The secure bustle of High Street, with its friendly family shops, its (even in those times) busy streams of traffic and, above all, its smells — here near the beginning of our story, in 1911.

Descending to the Town by the highly embanked side of Castle Hill, Rose would jounce Willy about in his go-cart until, between mirth and panic, he was uncertain whether to vomit or wet his pants. Quite often he did both, giving Rose a brisk washing job at home-coming. The rest of us would swing madly on chains, running between holes in gracefully fluted posts, from the hill-top down to the Big School, where those tasty hot dinners were enjoyed by the train-children.

Below the grass bank careered the Bath Road traffic, until all at once we were at the bottom of the hill, seemingly inextricably entangled with a bewildering mass of motors, bicycles and tradesmen's vans. One of the gravest dangers for pedestrians was the hooves of dray-horses. But once safely across King Street, past the Methodist Church and having come through the traffic pouring out of Marlow Road, we joined the secure bustle of High Street, with its friendly family shops, its (even in those times) busy streams of traffic and, above all, its smells.

Those unforgettable smells! Nicholsons' brewery for a start. One really deep breath of that had your head rotating on your neck like an intoxicated ventriloquist's dummy. In winter the pong blew down viciously from ventilators and chimney stacks, especially if the wind happened to be from the north. Its extensive frontage had about it an air of engaging dottiness. Uprightly oval shop windows were separated by darkly mottled columns, resembling petrified, highly polished cylinders of black pudding; supported on waist-high plinths and separated by a series of glacis, they gave a general impression of architectural frivolity, of merrily unashamed bad taste. I had never heard of such an exotic word as 'aesthetic' and only associated bad taste with comments by ma's friends concerning each others' new garments. However, I knew that that brewery elevation, together with its lead-capped Tudoresque towers, like the over-massive balustrade to Queen Anne's front door, and the violently red brick of the new Police Station on the corner of the Broadway, made me uncomfortable. Children *know* with their brand-spanking new instincts.

Across the Street, adjacent to Saunders' the butchers, gaped the entrance to a passage known to me and my siblings as Stinkey-Boys'-Hole. It was utterly pestilential, as if a dragon, gorged to repletion on corruption, had laid himself down somewhere up that court to sleep it off — a flatulent dragon, whose breath was foulest miasma. In fact on Wednesday, Mr Saunders' animals were murdered there and turned into meat in a ghastly covered yard. The stench never really cleared. A popular game with the urchins from the Barracks — a terrible nearby slum - was to defy each other to walk (not run) with breath held the entire length of this noisome thoroughfare, and it was nothing to come upon a dozen or two of these masochists leaning, half asphyxiated, against the wall in West Street. Why such things were tolerated in a smart town like Maidenhead is difficult to perceive. A butcher guilty of a similar offence today would soon be up before the Beaks. But there....I suppose that over half the more considerable shop-keepers constituted the Beakery, and it was a case of live and let live. Almost all of them had enjoyed Mayoral office at some time or another — some of them twice or even five times, like Mr Tom Stuchberry. My father's employer, Mr C.T. Chamberlain, had had two goes at it, and was a JP to boot.

Indelibly associated with Mooghie, High Street opens out by the Bear Hotel, where the bark effigy appeared to be nesting.

His premises almost faced Stinky - Boys' - Hole and represented its perfect olfactory antithesis. Mr C.T. Chamberlain was a Court Hairdresser and Perfumier. My father was manager of his ladies' department upstairs, and did very well on account of his undoubted artistry, his slim elegance, and because he was macho with it, in a steely, nimble kind of way. It reflects, I know, rather badly upon my filial

25

piety that later, when better informed, I saw him sometimes as a Capo di Lazzaroni; a sort of super hit-man of Naples. Assuredly there lurked somewhere behind his suave exterior something dangerous, some half-definable, half-amiable menace. The women went for it like mad.

There issued, sometimes gushed from Mr Chamberlain's portals, warm and delicious fragrances. Coty, Houbigant, duBarry, Mornay, the scent of Abdullah cigarettes mingled with a sinister undertone of simmering henna-paste and another aroma, astringent, toasty, of baking borax from the perming. You could smell it from as far away as Dysons' piano shop.

C.T. Chamberlain's voice rolled forth like a rich syrup, as if he had swallowed a crystallized Elva's plum and was sweetly savouring a pleasant strangulation. He himself was a tallish and portly person, pink as a wax-work. His false teeth flashed like polished porcelain when he smiled, rendering his tightly-waved hair and moustache, both dyed a glossless and intense black, shockingly funereal. Over twinkling gold pince-nez, he beamed with egregious patronage on the world around him. On everything, animal, vegetable and mineral, he beamed. The entire universe he charmed and placated at the same time. Only one single person he truly loved and wholly respected - himself. Once he gave me the shock my young life by walking, his legs very close together, the length of his little side-passage, breaking uninterrupted wind the whole way. Deep, muffled as thunder threatening on a sultry summer afternoon, I counted up to twenty-seven, before he swerved off into Nicholson's yard, still detonating.

To return to our muttons: the High Street redolences. Hanging on to Willy's go-cart I would sometimes shut my eyes when the fancy took me and read them like a rich, eventful book. The Maypole and the Home and Colonial were tasty and piquant with tea and coffee, fresh with butter, pungent with cheeses. Budgen, the ironmonger, breathed an essentially practical assortment of whiffs: oiled farm and garden machinery, creosoted garden string and cherry-tree netting. Stuchburys' exhaled a flat, warm blandness of sacked-up

Up High Street around 1927, was the lady with the bike about to meet my father?

seeds, corn-grains, rolled oats and oil-cake. Timothy-Whites' and Upsons' hung a hygienic cloud of rich antisepsis and prophilaxis before our noses. Spindlers drove you out of your mind with a mad greediness. Never anywhere else on this earth were produced such éclairs, such profiteroles, such sumptuous macaroons, cream-horns and iced cream-slices!

But now I opened my eyes. Here was Colebrookes and everything from sea and tree was there before your eyes and nose: fish in one great open window — fruit in the other. The treasures of the ocean in its prodigal entirety were there, prostrate in beds of ice that cooled the air suddenly and gave one a tiny pain in the back of the neck. Hoses trickled pellucid streams down the slope of the marble. Shrimps, lobsters, winkles and whelks; crabs, ugly cod and hake; whiting performing their dead contortionist act. And the salmon and daintily striated scallops! And the fruit, too. In summer the melons and cantaloupes and other glories were all arranged by those artist-shopkeepers and their assistants. And over all the piercing sweetness of strawberries! It was wonderful, all of it — even in winter, when the two predominating scents were those of Spanish chestnuts and clean-scrubbed celery fresh from the local nurseries. I have never quite recovered from Colebrookes' Cornucopian treasure-house. It has been for me the archetype of all such shops — the Victorian principle of luxury shopping, with drawing room manners.

And so we turned for home, making our calls on the way back. C.T. Chamberlain, neat and spruce in alpaca jacket, pin striped trousers and twinkling small boots, was there posted just inside his door; erect, motionless, meditative. 'Like something in Madam Two-Swords', said Rose, and indeed he might have been one of those officials in effigy, set there as a practical joke upon information-seeking visitors. I know this: at my first reading of Daisy Ashford's *Young Visitors* I knew who he really was. He was Mr Saltina.

So, up the hill we dragged ourselves, trawling our feet and complaining. Willy's monotonous whine might have had Pa's fingers itching. We had paid the books, we were fed up with the afternoon, and we wanted, above all things, our tea.

3

Transports of Delight

If I had known how lovely she would become, would I have taken her so for granted? When I whizzed by on my bicycle and she advanced so eagerly to the very pavements edge to greet me, how cavalierly had I cast her a casual wave and passed on. Then later, when we became half sweethearts, half chums, it was, compared to this, mere light romance, just having the satisfaction of possessing a girl-friend, a status-symbol, as it were. I realized now, and sharply, what a blow it might have been had I lost her in those days, how generously she had considered my feeling, never given me cause for jealously or unhappiness, always and unswervingly loyal from the moment in front of the fire at Queen Anne when the robin sang, to this afternoon when she suddenly appeared in her strange, new, haunting beauty.

A sweet breeze rippled the ivy of the Bear Hotel where, above the main door, the bark effigy appeared to be nesting. It blew their light frocks into the curves of their legs, sculpturally, excitingly. Passers-by stared, it seemed to me, in wonder. All cock-a-hoop, I was, proud as Punch. I hadn't a sou for train-fare, and that had me sweating a bit, but at least I had on my better suit and a clean shirt. I thanked the Lord that, despite the heat, my feet were fresh as daisies. Unlike poor Victor, I was lucky that way.

My concern proved to have been unnecesssary. Mrs Campbell bought my ticket for me. I breathed again. 'Mum's privilege,' she smiled. 'I dare say you're flat-broke. Sons are rarely treated so well as girls in the matter of pocket-money. I've noticed it repeatedly. Mooghie, dear, you have got a wrinkle in your stocking.'

With excruciating tact, I gazed away down Station Approach to the Victorian Tudor Jubilee clock. It said half past five. I must ring up Pa as soon as I got to Cygnet Green. The taxis were as old-fashioned and funny as ever, as were the small ugly offices where estate agents and coal merchants hung out. At the little gabled window beyond the tower sat Peter Timberlake, reading. Ma had once kept a twee little tea shop down there opposite the clock tower. It was 'the thing' at one time, and involved the wearing of a cute smocked overall, a supply of cheap and cheerful chairs and tables, and a few expensive lines in chocolates exhibited in wooden trays on slender legs. How those chairs would creak under the weight of those blazered bums, straight off the river and ready for a nice refreshing cuppa! Had they or their dainty escorts been vouchsafed one look back-stage, where the smelly little sink kept close company with the suspect lavatory, where the handled ice-cream freezer was kept, what sort of appetite would they have had for the paste sandwiches, pastries and strawberry ices?

Ma, in her careless, impulsive way had got fed up and let it go for a song. It interfered with her jaunts to Ascot and Goodwood with her friend, Nessie Spindler. It wouldn't, as she put it, let her call her soul her own.

Hearing laughter I turned around.

'Galahad,' mocked Muriel. 'It was only at my ankle, silly.'

'What a nice, darling boy,' remarked her mother.

'He always was,' said Muriel.

Up the subway their heels tip-tapped prettily; their laughter rang like temple bells. The place always stank of wet cardboard and fish, rumbled and roared with porters' trolleys or a passing train. A look up showed you the grey shimmer of its wheels through the dirty glass of the platform's side. When one stopped, the porters would bellow, 'Maid'ned! Maid'ned!' And in a moment, a storm of footsteps would rush down the stairways and voices create a hell of noise and confusion; milk-churns would clank and rattle.

Up on platform one we encountered Flatbury and Wynnd of the upper fifth: suspect lingerers behind the bike-sheds — stinkards both. They made disobliging remarks behind their hands at sight of me in such ravishing society. I felt like a Baron of the land, regarding them de haut en bas as they well deserved, the dirty dogs!

'How does it feel, getting on the train with me instead of just seeing me off?' asked Muriel. I shot her mother a swift glance. Her return look was quizzical.

How chairs would creak under blazered bums, straight off the river and ready for a nice cup of tea!

'God knows, dear boy, you've been invited often enough. I could have killed you sometimes when Mooghie came home looking wretched with disappointment because you had turned her down.'

I flushed. It was all too true. With the flimsiest, sometimes cynical pretexts I had wriggled out of her invitations; but there: I had treated others in just the same way. I had become anti-social. I had preferred our little tea-parties at the shop in Station Approach to being formally entertained by her parents.

31

'Please don't, mummy. He was just shy, that's all. We got used to our little parties at Marie's, didn't we? They were such fun.'

The carriage was sweet with their scents. Even that stink of sour steam and hard-boiled eggs which tended to haunt railway compartments in the steam age yielded to their fragrances.

'Will you mind if I have a tiny snooze, dears. I've a slight head coming on. I really promise not to snore. So repulsive.' And off she drifted, softly as an evening primrose closing its petals at sunrise.

'Mum's always a little souffrante after the pictures,' said Muriel. 'I do hope she won't wake up with a migraine,' she can be hell with a really bad one.'

The whistle blew. The train chuffed out of the Station. The Jubilee clock disappeared behind roof-tops. Soon we thundered across the Sounding Arch, then on past the Hall's Distemper men on their eternal tramp across the fields with their plank, where cows flicked their tails by the stream. Muriel gave me an impish, uncertain grin. She was, with her thinner cheeks and their high bones, absolutely stunning. 'Darling,' she whispered tremulously, 'Come and kiss me.' I got to my feet and bent shakily forward. Slowly, as though meeting in a heavenly dream, our faces met, and then our lips. I felt her soft fingers cupping my hot cheeks. Her kiss was like a bite at a passion fruit: divinely soft and yielding, gathered into a sweet, sensuous cushion.

She had never kissed me like that before. I nearly keeled over.

And so I came to our little Town Hall. It had six ionic columns below and an equal number of pilasters in the same style above, with three Venetian windows. The entrance was dingy and drab but redeemed by another fetish of mine: a single, fat pillar which gave a tactile impression of being moulded in the same clay from which a school-boy's marbles are made. Slightly viscid to the fingers in wet weather, it lurked in the dimness, minatory, authoritative, drawing towards itself the eager finger I stretched forth in a respectful touch of propitiation. I emerged from the performance of this ritual to see Mr Spindler dismounting at the door of his father's shop from his majestic bicycle. Immediately perceiving me, he shouted across the street:

'You're going to be in awful trouble, old chap. You get a move on or y'r dad's going to skin you alive. Y'r train leaves in a couple of hours — or had you forgotten?'

'Oh, Lor!' I took a hurried look up at the Town Hall clock in its queer bit of mansard roof. 'Oh, glory be!'

I'd taken close on three hours dawdling and dreaming from Taplow.

'Thanks, Mr Spindler, thanks!' I cried and took to my heels. Now there would be the very devil of a row with Pa. He was bound to blame me for lack of enthusiasm over the holiday he was about to provide, from a flourishing bit of business done on the side.

Nevertheless, I did pause a moment at Queen Street. Yesterday afternoon, that's the way we had taken towards the Station. I screwed up my eyes in a wrenching effort of will to conjure up our three yesterday's ghosts: Muriel in her Chinese frock of pale yellow, with her blonde hair piled up; her lovely mother, Mediterraneanly blue-black of hair, pale rose of skin, exquisitely shingled, in a black cotton frock printed with a pattern of white and red roses, and both gifted with almost identically slim, shapely legs. Between them, myself, looking by contrast a terribly sawny twit.

Useless. It is only on the screen that these captivating hallucinations oblige the wistful hero.

I began to trot up High Street, by now extremely anxious. And whom should I espy emerging from Stinkey-Boys'-Hole but Mr Bickly, our baker's roundsman, with his basket of buns over his arm and his super-smart cord breeches. One more fetish of mine.

'Hi, Mr Bickly,' I shouted above the traffic. 'Hi, how about a lift for a pal?'

He jerked a large curved thumb. 'Hop in, mate.'

Chugging slowly but steadily up Castle Hill in the tinny little G.W.K., smelling about evenly of warm new loaves and exhaust smoke, it seemed in retrospect a happy thought that had directed me to propitiate my Town Hall pillar. It had, I was entirely convinced, got me this lucky lift home.

At the top of Gordon Road Mr Bickly let me off outside Mr Keiller's grocery shop and here dire disaster struck. Big-Boy sprang out as though from an ambush, flourishing before my nose a pair of enormous fists: knobbly as bludgeons, ingrained with timeless dirt. Behind the fists, eyes resembling blood-shot marbles were as menacing as the contemptuous smile playing over carious teeth.

'Go on, college-chump,' he growled. "It me!'

My rock ahead in life....! My unholy terror! All the kids round our way feared and fled him, as well they might. I was, alas, the one he had to pick on, his preordained victim, that was me, scapegoat for the rest.

In fact he was no longer 'Big-Boy' because four years had elapsed since he first tormented me. I had grown to be a good half head taller than him. There must have been something about me that griped him badly — my misleadingly delicate exterior perhaps, or my bourgeois accent. Who can tell where these predetermined hates have their beginnings? Whatever their provenance, his clear intention was to provoke me into first blow, thus giving him carte-blanche to mangle me at his pleasure. By God! he scared me into fits with his dreadful, squat brutality.

I had the choice of five ways home from the County Boys School but, no matter how I varied them, at least once in the week mine enemy found me out — usually when my young brothers and Renee were nearby to witness the humiliation. When I sagely declined to hit him, he had a deft way of hooking one of his legs behind both of mine, and pushing me over backwards. I fell for it every time.

Yet, despite my slenderness and the timidity he made me feel, I knew myself to be the stronger of the two physically, and much more resourceful mentally. Intuition told me that the sheer weight of the lout's brutishness and hate must prevail against whatever virtues I might possess. He hated and meant to hurt. I submitted out of habit. It was like paying tribute to a dangerous bandit. And let there be no mistake: he was dangerous. He lived in the then squalor and poverty of College Glen and, furthermore, smelt of it. Not improbably he divined my repulsion for his person and rather naturally resented it.

Well, this morning he was on to a rotten orange. His luck had run out. I looked not into his bull's eyes but to the iron railings and crude red brick wall of Gordon Road School. The heat, now intense, shimmered over them in a devil's dance. Between my shoulder-blades fear made the sweat run. I thought of Mooghie under the Lumie Tree last night: ethereally lovely in the summer lightning's fitful glow, her eyes closed, golden lashes fringing her cheeks, lips pouted for kissing....Supposing, just supposing, we were to encounter this pitiless hooligan in some solitary place....the Thicket or Burnham Beeches perhaps — imagination withered at the bare idea.

He gave me a thump in the chest. Again our eyes met. By some subtle instinct I perceived that, with all his rank coarseness, he sensed a change from my usual reaction; a change that threw him momentarily off balance. His pupils gave one nervous flicker. Yet, 'Gow on Nancy — 'it me,' he persisted. ''It me!'

So I did. First, one-two in the bread-basket; then, as he folded up, another to tap his claret. There was a lot of it. His nose was a squash. Blood gushed from between his dirty fingers as he lay upon the blistering tarmac of the side-walk, where he had so often laid me. What on earth is it that arouses one's pity for a fallen bully's tears? Why does one feel almost equal shame in the role of either lion or worm?

I held out my hand but he scrambled unaided to his feet, the fight gone out of him, but not the hate.

'You want to shake hands?' I asked him.

'Shi' in yer bloody 'and,' he snuffled and blubbered. 'You wait till next time, mate!'

'Please yourself,' I replied. 'But touch me again or either of my young brothers and I'll bash the rest of your face in — mate.'

All at once I was tired of the whole thing; utterly failing in exultation. I turned for home. A sordid scrap in the open street, and the night before Mooghie had sung to us Rachmaninov's *Daisies* to her own exquisite guitar accompaniment. What a space that scrap with Big-Boy had placed between heaven and the banal everyday of Gordon Road. Never mind. Pleasure came to mingle with shame. I had found my courage. I half expected a parting stone, but a look back showed me my late tormentor's form rounding the bend into College Glen. Dirty handkerchief sopping away at his nasal ruin he was sobbing his heart out, the poor bastard. The worm had turned as worms so frequently do, given just the right sort of kick up the backside. His bully's pride was in the dirt. But he had had a good run for his money.

Neighbours were at their gates. A moment ago the place had been like the grave. Without a word, I unlatched our Gordon Road gate, clattering it to behind me, leaving the Streets, whose startling blue-eyed, grey haired likeness to one another suggested a Pharaonic marriage, Mrs Carter, whose son was in prison, the Rowes, who represented in the human world the praying mantis, and poor old Mr Dean, leaning his chin upon the handle of his rake to tongue-wag over my extraordinary show of spirit and its bloody outcome.

The latter Pa had put out of bounds. One of Pa's untouchables, he was, with his cap dead straight on his grizzled skull, his steel-rimmed spectacles glinting, and his metallic teeth on full show as, with a lazy, lascivious smile, he watched the little kids passing schoolwards from under the peak of his greasy old cap. Not that his cap was not perfectly clean inside, but the habit of lifting it by the peak to every passing lady had just made that peak into another colour entirely.

One peep at Pa sufficed. I was in for a dressing-down. So I sat myself down to bacon and eggs and fell to. He wanted a row....he should have the initiative. Ma wore her Norfolk conflict-mask: iron-browed, the lower lip forcing up the upper, to call to mind an old-fashioned mantlepiece. A pretty pair.

I fear I disappointed them: blandly asking pardon for my unpunctuality, assuring them I had breakfasted, confounding them with mock-solemn urbanity. I was presuming, for Pa had had the parental decency to stop socking me when I reached the age of fourteen. Qui s'excuse, s'accuse. Such had been my way for too long. I could almost hear them wondering what had happened to my stammered excuses, self-justification and, finally, hot, ungovernable, ineffectual temper. They could wonder in vain. I had kissed my woman and slapped my man.

I had, I felt, grown up.

'You haven't even left yourself sufficient time to bathe your foul body,' nagged Pa relentlessly. 'That will be a fine treat for Mrs Grintforth's clean sheets, won't it?'

I patted my chest. 'All sweet and clean as a nut,' I said smugly. 'Bathed last night and this morning too.'

'What?'

'They are very particular people at Mariposa.' 'As unhealthy as unnecessary!' riposted Pa smartly. 'Saps the strength enervates the nervous system, removes a great part of the skin's essential oils. It — '

'Muriel's father is a doctor,' I broke in. 'He should know what's what, shouldn't he?'

Pa sprang to the saddle of his hobby-horse. 'Phah!' The worst old cranks of the lot! Look how they bundled me off to Russia after my peritonitis!' He put on the stuffily sadistic expression of a Lyceum Victorian saw-bones. ' "Ho-Ho! Here's a pulse! He's warm as well! And, by God, he's breathing! He'll do — off he goes san fairy anne!" Chah! don't talk to me about doctors! They're worse than the black beetles!' Fuming, my eccentric time-keeping forgotten, he strode violently from the room, pausing only to trip up over Tony's go-cart in the passage.

'What do they call their house?' Ma loosened her lips to enquire.

'Mariposa,' I said. 'Pretty, eh?'

'Quite nice,' she commented. 'Sounds like a flower of some sort.'

'It's Spanish for butterfly.'

'Better than most of the stupid names up and down the Avenue. Dun Romin, Mon Repos and there's that silly ass up near Cromwell Road who has called his Lebam — that's Mabel spelt backwards!' She poured me more coffee. 'You'd better get any extra things you'll need packed as soon as you're finished.'

My brothers returned. They had been across the Avenue to say farewell to the Spindlers. Victor was plaintive. 'They're off on a picnic to the Lovely-Fields,' he grumbled. 'Renee and Nadia and Hughie. I wish I were going. They're starting to cut wheat. Cor!'

Ma's eyes fired. She cried:

'You thankless boy, when your poor father has toiled like a galley-slave to give you a splendid holiday at Lowes-toft! Some children never get a holiday from one year's end to the other. Do you know that?'

'Lucky old them!' Victor nimbly dodged the maternal palm. 'Only joking, mother, dear.'

'I should hope so too! Your poor father with three great boys to bring up and get out into the world....!'

'Rather a good job he stopped at we three. We'd have come off pretty badly if — '

'By the way,' I interrupted. 'You can cut through the Glen to get to the baths from now on.'

'What? with that dangerous maniac lurking there? Don't make me laugh.'

'Big-Boy's done for,' I announced casually. 'I've just come from spifflicating him.'

'You've what?'

'I've whacked him. His pride is crouching in the dirt.'

'Liar! I bet you cowered in the gutter and let him kick you.'

'Alright, just you pop down the Glen and take a look at his ugly red conk. You'll find it's lovely crimson by now. Here, take a gander at my knuckles then, if you don't believe me.'

'My God!' Victor exclaimed. 'You're a bloody hero after all!'

'He's a what?' demanded Pa returning to the scene.

'A hero. He's licked Big-Boy Baker down the Glen. The reign of terror is over. Hurrah!'

Pa looked at me with bemused wonder. 'You've actually tanned that unbalanced young thug from the Glen? Swop me a bob I didn't think you had it in you. Good for you, old son!'

It didn't seem to occur to him that I might have risked smashing my knuckles on the eve of my musical examination.

Across the Avenue lived the Spindlers — Renee, here with the Woolf boys: author, Victor and, in the front, Tony.

Mother clasped at her nose-bridge convulsively. 'One of my boys involved in a vulgar street-brawl!' she cried in one of her favourite character-parts.

'The Lady Constance,' whispered Victor behind his hand.

'Did he bleed much?' Tony wanted to know.

'Like a stuck pig,' I reassured him. 'Enough to satisfy even you, you blood-thirsty little rotter.'

I went upstairs. From my back-bedroom window, where the rising sun had flaked away the grey-green paint; over the arching boughs of our cherry-trees; beyond the Thames Valley, the distant hills lay dreaming in that halcyon late summer weather: blue-grey and mysterious. Somewhere beyond that magnetic prospect nestled the rustic fairyland of Cygnet Green and Mariposa, and Mooghie in all the romantic, virginal splendour of her new young womanhood, all her hitherto unsuspected talents — and the Lumie Tree. Before I would be able to taste once more the delights of the enchanted territory, I saw before me, like a ravaged landscape, thorny, weed-grown and rank, two weeks of sea-side tedium at Lowestoft: dullest of resorts, where fish stank and skinning winds suited only to Vikings and fisher girls made bathing a martyrdom, and even the shrimps boiled down to a drab and mottled brown. I could have cried my bloody eyes out at the prospect. Instead, I had a good swear, smoked a couple of Pasha cigarettes, and allowed my mind to drift away to Mooghie's azure house-gown, as we danced to *Blue Skies* in her mother's drawing-room. This swirling garment gave out to every movement she made of her lithe body a ghostly memory, a dream of Italian jessamines and a frou-frou that resembled the whisper of a gigantic shower of rose-petals: an illusion fostered by the perfume wafting from the wide bowls of floating rose-heads.

4

Down the Avenue

From Robert Taylor's pretty bridge to the sweet-scented Thicket, Maidenhead occupied a good three miles of the main Bath Road. In the main coaching was its original raison d'etre, its bridge its fortune until the Victorians came with trade breweries and piety to turn everything inside-out and upside-down. They made a thorough job of it too. Meadows and orchards they covered with their shops and warehouses and counting-houses. Farmland and pastures they buried in not unattractive suburbs. In the holes and corners and back-alleys their commercial architecture left, slums began to fester and ferment. When I was a little boy the impetus of their enterprise had scarce begun to slacken. In Edwardian times, on the low ground beside and near the River, peerage and stage came together in a frothy welter of pleasure, frivolity, adultery and sometimes marriage. Aristocratic families rejuvenated themselves with new blood, and a renewal of their occasionally disastrously failing looks. In winter, as if to bring down a judgement upon their sinning, old Father Thames would flood his banks, to inundate ground floors and, in the process, bring misery to the poor devils who dwelt in poor streets fringing the Town Moor, proving just one more time that the innocent suffer with the guilty. On a day of high flood in the mid-twenties, a certain Miss May Ruffel, a baker's daughter in Bridge Road, and prominent in the Town swimming-club, swam for a wager from her father's shop doorway up to Chapel Arches, thereby almost losing her amateur status. She made the front page too.

The Victorians were wiser. They built on the high ground of Castle Hill, and beyond towards Maidenhead Thicket. To them I am forever grateful, for All Saints Avenue and the nice little house, dated 1882, where my siblings and I spent our childhood, with its long narrowish garden and mixed fruit-trees in a row, its smooth lawn and flower-beds surrounded by climbing roses on trellises. At the bottom there was a kitchen-garden smelling of caterpillars and cabbages in early autumn, and of sweet peas and potato haulms in early summer. The house stood on a corner, and its front faced the Avenue, and there, in the summer months in a cosy little garden, Ma would entertain her friends to tea and whist.

Victorians, Edwardians....now we neo-Georgians took up the town's story, pursuing it at the decorous jog-trot we thought bade fair to go on forever and a day.

But after the war came the slump. There was discontent, dirt and dislike behind the bland facade. Areas like the Barracks and Moffet Street in particular exuded strange, alien stinks of poverty. Soot, smoke, damply-rotting brickwork and a multitude of whiffs of poor food cooked as best it might be mingled with the ubiquitous odour of the brewery. Every other building seemed to be a pub bearing the red and gold sign-board of Nicholson. Passing them you were aware of gruff voices from within pitched in the ugly dialect of urban Berkshire. From their doors emanated a foxy reek, mixed with human sweat and beer gone stale.

Once, at a Christmas party at an ancient coaching inn in Bridge Street, losing my way to the lavatory, I came upon a monumentally luxurious sofa at the end of a carpeted passage way. Tapestried curtains hung behind it. Together they had an air of forbidding, rather sinister pomp, sufficient to arouse a boy's curiosity. I satisfied mine by lifting the curtain a bit, and promptly wished I had not.

A street lamp showed broken windows and bins overflowing with rubbish and filth onto the melting snow. A communal pump dripped like a running nose, and a rough creature with yorkers at his knees held the head of a vomiting girl over a drain. Here and there a candle guttered behind ragged net curtains.

I returned to the party with a queasy stomach. Behind a door I had come upon an enormous side of beef squeezed between two boards by heavy iron weights. No wonder the poorer Council School kids kicked hell out of our smug-looking little legs.

We had been lucky. Pa returned from Russia to find his job not only secure but much better paid. His absence, if it had not made C.T. Chamberlain's heart grow fonder, had loosened his purse strings a trifle. Pa had gone to the wars and people missed him, and many decided to go somewhere else until his

*Maidenhead occupied a good three miles of the Bath Road —
coaching was its raison d'etre . . . its bridge its fortune: the
tollgate and Bridge House guarded the crossing.*

return. His reputation found itself much enhanced by the unusual nature of his war-service, and that livid scar across the back of his hand. He had fought the bolshies, which went down well with his patrician clientele, and had, moreover, gone down with his ship off the Orkney Islands, a mere cable's length from the spot where Lord Kitchener went to the fishes in the *Hampshire*, together with his pointing finger and manic eye. Pa popped up in his brave, macho survivor's way, to be picked up in a matter of minutes. Now, as he twirled his marcel-irons, making it look like a conjuring trick, his scar glinting glabrously in the electric light, his fine aquiline nose hovering above them, some of these women must have thought him a queer kind of Figaro. An odd sort of coiffeur altogether was my old man. Unfortunately, he was totally unambitious, but brilliantly convivial — a dangerous combination. As a father, he was superb, until one by one we reached adolescence, when he threw up his hands in bewildered dismay and gave up coping. His nervousness in case I put some girl or other in trouble was phobic, and funny indeed. Had Ma born him girls instead of boys it would have been a case of tin drawers all round.

There was something essentially ecclesiastical about All Saints Avenue. For a start it was nearly half a mile in length, dominated from the Bath Road end by the handsome Tractarian Church of G.E. Street. Silver-grey was its spire, sharp as a needle. Its tower, decorated by coloured strings of brick, was pierced by the bell-tower's louvres, and these like ancient eyes, seemed to observe every detail of our goings forth and comings in. There reigned over us the perpetual illusion of living in a vast outdoor church, an externalized projection of that edifice's interior: an illusion reinforced by two ranks of magnificent horse-chestnut trees, assorted pink and white, lining each side of the Avenue, strongly suggesting a massively soaring cathedral nave.

By mentally abolishing all side-roads saving the main road to Bath, and furthermore delimiting that dangerous highway to five hundred yards or so in either direction, I ended by conceiving of the Avenue as a vast topographical sign of the Cross. And when crazy old Mrs Nettles paused half-way across the road to genuflect churchwards, though neighbours were derisive behind their curtains, I was inclined to approve her action on secular grounds, as indicating her independence of behaviour as well as proving my imagination's logic. I was already well on the royal road to perdition, for Pa had early made an agnostic of me. 'Black beetles' was his name for them, and sometimes 'collared cockroaches.' Well I recall his eyes, flaming like blue saucers after his brush with death on the operating-table, and his long dismissive finger pointing poor Reverend Maghee to the door of the Ward when he came, with all the tact of the cleric, during our visiting time, offering his Anglican comforts to the sick and the sorry! Sick and sorry...! Old Pa was more like a condottiere of the Italian Rinascimento dismissing a bothersome priestling than a recently hem-stitched hairdresser with a tube creeping out of his guts like a snake. My old man was a most peculiar hairdresser.

In Edwardian times, peerage and stage came together in a frothy welter of pleasure, frivolity, adultery and sometimes marriage. The Thames Hotel welcomed the carriage trade .

We had few neighbours of importance — only Councillor Norkett, designer of the famous Norkett Dam, ex-Mayor and, inevitably, present Magistrate. My friend, Teddy Norkett in Cromwell Road, boasted constantly of 'me Grampy' and built him up into a figure of terror. I see him now, trotting like an obsequious outrider, his boots ringing in equine manner on the paving stones, in front of a small, bearded old gentleman on a slow green bicycle and crying out in a voice of doom, 'look out Hubert, look out! — ME GRAMPY!'

And I did indeed look out because, as a Justice of the Peace, he held in his hand the terrible power to condemn delinquent

45

youth to the birch; an appalling chastisement which concluded with the rubbing of salt into the blood-oozing weals. Goodness only knows what impelled C.T. Chamberlain to describe for me in such realistic detail this gruesome wage of sin while on a visit of comfort to Ma, while Pa was away in Archangel. I was not aware of having notably sinned in the recent past. Why then this quite gratuitous little lecture? Could he, perhaps, have been a bit of an old sadist on the quiet for all his benevolent exterior; for all his wide, tight, cherry-lipped smile?

It was in Bath Road that the big shots lived in handsome houses built by their fathers or grandfathers. The grounds belonging to these splendid Regency-style dwellings were extensive and beautiful. One had a tall palm on its south side, which seemed to lead a charmed life unextinguishable by Thames Valley frosts or fogs, quite obviously sharing a beneficent Providence with its proprietor, whose forebear had planted it with characteristic optimism, Faith, Hope and Charity.

We of the Avenue, though perfectly aware of our relative nonentity, stoutly nourished the pride that sustains all the Lupin Pooters and Murray Poshes of this world. We paid our way, we dressed respectably, we maintained a comme-il-faut standard of behaviour and decorum. In fact we considered ourselves quite the equals of the Bath Road dwellers, if not so well-off. The few social bad-apples such as the Shrubsoles, whose sire was a Corporation navvy, wore yorkers and smoked a foul cutty-pipe, were politely ignored, a fact that didn't appear to affect them overmuch. Their cottages were of smoky brown brick, relics of a period when farmland surrounded them. Autocthonous they looked and their inhabitants appropriately aboriginal. We of the petit bourgeoisie looked to the more well-to-do families at the Avenue's extremities to bolster our social self-confidence, though a large percentage of these occupied extremely constricted quarters and no longer fretted over social distinctions at all. The churchyard enclosed the unrealised ambitions of some and the cemetery at the Courthouse Road end those of the rest.

Of Death and Judgement, Heaven and Hell
Who oft doth think must needs die well.

So wrote Sir Walter Raleigh in the Tower, and it was to Maidenhead they brought him for his trial for treason against that most unpleasant monarch, James I, in 1603. The Plague was most probably in London at the time and the judges windy about it. This time they found him guiltless. There was an appealing aptness to we of the Avenue about his two immortal lines. Two well-populated grave-yards: and a church whose steeple shot Heavenwards like a surrealistic finger kept us in mind of his powerfully pious words. We should have made good diers.

Old Edward Spindler did not inhabit Bath Road, though he was an original founder-father of our High Street commerce. His son, Renee and Jim's father, elderly himself, lived opposite to us but in a newer house. It had a bathroom, Art Nouveau decorations and a garden with a view from its bottom over a cornfield towards the workhouse, euphemistically known as the Union. Squatting on the pig-sty roof (it was war-time and the cultivations of live edibles almost de rigeur) I was moved to tears by a sunset the like of which I have never since seen. I date the beginning of any poetry there is in me from that moment.

I wonder how many sunsets had squeezed a tear out of Grandpa Spindler's eye. It would have been a small, flinty one no doubt; a sort of lachrimal constipation. Spindler and Sons, it said above the door, and Spindler and Sons he intended it should remain while there was a puff of breath in his body. Stocky, white-haired, lame and peremptory, he rumbled and stumped with the help of a cudgel-like stick up and down the cobbled yard in West Street, white moustache bristling, grumbling and burping away like an untrustworthy volcano unwillingly containing its lava.

Rus in urbes: that was Spindler's yard. Odours of horse-dung, hay, oats and dust hung about the lofts and outhouses and the cobbled yard in front of the half-doors where Ed and Ted Spindler worked at confectionery and bread respectively.

A tall, thin man cooked meat for the restaurant and a short, fat apprentice cleaned and prepared the vegetables with a sufficient encouragement of kicks and clips around the ears. You would scarcely have believed that a matter of a few yards separated this Dickensian kitchen-scene from the sophisticated Edwardian restaurant where Jilly Durrant, Renee's pretty cousin, managed the small staff of waitresses who called everybody female 'Madame', everybody male 'Sir', with an occasional 'My Lord'. Napery was snow-white, cutlery gleamed like moonshine and the dark mulberry wall-paper glowed warmly n the light of shaded sconces. There it was: the discipline and dignified welcome, the pleasant amenity that never stepped out of line, never forgot its place or its self-respect.

The firm delivered by dog-cart. Their chief driver was a snappy young spinster called Mary Porson, and one of the saddest sights I ever beheld was her favourite pony, Toby, his lips slackened and loose in death, exposing the long stained teeth, stripped of his harness, his head across the weeping woman's knees. Castle Hill had proved too much for him at last, and was now strewn with buns and cottage loaves. Just one more working horse had shown that it had a heart to be broken.

When, at long last, Grandpa Spindler went to see how his ancestors had made out, Renee's father opened up on his own account, a hundred yards away in Queen Street, just opposite to The Hand and Flowers, and filled the entire slum behind (with quite unconscious cruelty) with a paradisal smell of cooking and baking, making up in part by baking, free of charge, their meagre weekly joints. He prospered exceedingly. In the fullness of time, Renee wed and had three little girls, one after the other, her father followed the old volcano and Jim took over. Quite soon it became clear that he was not really up to it. He hadn't the flair or the energy. The High Street ideal floundered and then faded. Jim sold out and retired with his second wife to number 1 Westborough Road, which was near enough to Bath Road after all.

Thus, in defeat, Jimmy grasped a little victory. But one more family name vanished from the Town's commercial life.

For the second time in twenty-four hours I crossed Brunel's Sounding Arch, bidding a miserable 'au revoir' to punts, launches, and pleasure-steamers; the flannels, flowered frocks and beds of roses gracing velvety lawns, and the preening swans with their drab broods.

We had the compartment to ourselves. At Taplow the hot platforms were devoid of travellers. I dropped the window, looking to right and left. Alas, no Mooghie, as I had half-expected. A flat-belly shunted, spitting steam and cinders, and a porter half-slept, leaning upon the shafts of his truck. The Station-Master's roses scented the air, the bees and insects hummed busily. I caught a whiff of heliotrope.

Brunel's Sounding Arch, and beyond, Maidenhead Bridge
— au revoir to punts and preening swans.

The trains puffed onward. I pulled up the window and turned to survey my family. Tony was kneeling in his corner, breathing on the window, and drawing funny men in the condensation. Victor was reading *The Champion*. Ma, nibbling dark Meltis chocolate, was building herself one hell of a migraine, Pa's beautiful grey flannel suit, dark violet neck-tie and stiff white collar resolutely disclaimed all association with

Victor's perforated sandals, Willy's spade and pail, and Ma's rather dowdily unsuitable holiday cloche, in which she looked not unlike the press photographs of Mrs Kate Merrick emerging from Holloway Gaol. You wouldn't get Pa into holiday garb until the very starting-line of holiday. His expensive black trilby rested demurely in the rack above his head. He slept, wearing a faint smile as if dreaming agreeably. Of his latest flame, I wondered, or the motor-car he yearned to possess? Of being well rid of us all? Or was his somnolent grimace just one of alcoholic fatuity?

There should have been a five-minute wait at Slough. Instead porters began to slam doors before Victor's breathless return just prevented Ma's lapsing into hysteria.

'Where's your *Magnet*?' I inquired, 'And what's in that bag?'

'You wretched, stupid boy!' nagged Ma, 'You might have been left behind.'

Victor looked excited. Ignoring Ma, he handed me the white paper bag. It contained a box of fifty Abdullah cigarettes and a leaf, green-gold and pinnate, a leaf of the *Robina Pseudoacacia*...the Lumie Tree!

Too thrilled for words I regarded him cretinously.

'Muriel! I just ran into her in time. My God, man, she's like a film star. Couldn't believe me eyes at first. And as gone on you as ever, you lucky dog, you! With Brenda she was, and she's not so dusty either. They looked super-modern too. Blimey, these duck-arsed skirts are great on girls with good long legs!' He cast a glance of absent disparagement at his mother's somewhat stocky limbs as she continued to nibble away at her Meltis chocolate.

An angelic messenger with uncouth sandals and the lining drooping from his cap like some ghastly brain damage; that is how my young brother appeared to me in that moment.

'Did-did she say anything-any message for me?'

'There wasn't time for much. She looked as though she might cry any minute. Said she was sorry to have missed you, told me to give you her love and you're to remember the Lumie Tree every night at ten o'clock. Then she gave me a little kiss and said pass it on, but I'm not kissing your ugly mug, old bean, so you may take that part as read. Brenda kissed me too,' he went on in surprised wonder, 'In spite of my kid's knickers and these repulsive anti-pong sandals. But there...I suppose I'm quite a well-set-up sort of a lad really.'

'You're a Grandee!' I exclaimed. 'You're a Baron of the land! When we get out of Liverpool Street we'll buzz off to the bogs for a smoke.'

'Good egg!' His eyes closed in an ecstasy of recollection. 'That scent of hers, old chap...! Like lovely tropical flowers — all waxy and sweet!'

Other people's holidays — pleasure steamers and the Riviera Hotel at Maidenhead.

'Italian Jasmines.'

He sighed. 'I'll never break wind again without shame — not after smelling her!'

'Give your father a dig,' directed Ma, 'He's about to snore at any second.'

'Give him a chance,' I objected, 'He'll only wake up cantankerous.'

'And perhaps he'll do his funny whistle through one nostril if we keep quiet,' said Tony. 'He does sometimes.'

But both our parents required jogging at Paddington Station. All at once it occurred to me how indefatigably they must have worked for this, our holiday.

At Colchester, damp chilly air crept into the carriage. By Ipswich the sky was the colour of ruined bread-pudding. Diss, and massive, clay-tinted clouds were rolling over from the west, and at Norwich rain lashed the carriage windows to streaming blindness.

But Lowestoft...! There had been a cloudburst, the ticket-collector told us. The lines between the platforms were flooding dongas. A few sparse groups waiting for trains might have been refugee doubters of the Divine Promise. The downpour had but recently abated. Such mass-misery there was of steam and fish and stinking wet clothes. Khaki sands, Punch and Judy in a roped-up tarpaulin coffin, sky and water indistinguishable one from the other and the harbour entrance lost in drifting sea-wrack.... Pa, hardy survivor and born campaigner, got us a taxi out of nowhere and we all climbed in.

'Spring comes to Lowestoft, 'intoned Victor with droll irony. 'What price Maidenhead and Muriel now, old lad? God save us all!'

'I've gone and left me spade and pail on the train,' said Tony.

'Oh, you little duffer,' whined poor Ma from behind her migraine-masque. 'Oh, dear, one more expense.'

'Oh, well...' he suddenly beamed around upon us. 'After all, who jolly well cares? Childish junk!'

I saw Pa's face fall. For a second it was gauntly sad. He was losing his third and last baby. 'He'll be smoking next,' he muttered and smiled wryly. 'Wenching too as like as not.'

'Don't be vulgar,' moaned Ma, but without much spirit of conviction.

'Phah!' ejaculated Pa in disgust.

The taxi drew up and we all got out. Just in time too. Ma was dreadfully sick behind Mrs Grintforth's forlorn and dripping laurel bushes.

That night the rain recommenced. No thunder or lightning or even much wind. Just a violent torrent that knocked a terrifying tune out of every surface there was. In the street it beat like massed cymbals; on garden soil it dully seethed and drummed; gutters became foaming Niagaras, and on a tin roof in the vicinity the rain hammered out a danse macabre. It was, in fact, dead frightening, and I wasn't sorry when Pa came up with a candle to see how we were faring up there aloft in the odd little garret Mrs Grintforth had assigned to Victor and me.

'You boys alright?'

'Yes,' I answered, 'We're not so bad. This rain makes the devil of a row overhead.'

'No water coming in or anything?'

Curiously enough there wasn't. Captain Grintforth, dead by drowning, would probably have declared the bizarre attic as well found.

'Victor's asleep then?'

'Went off soon as his head touched the pillow.'

'That boy could always get to sleep on a clothes-line. Lucky young dog. Good-night then, old chap. Your mother's out to the wide — and your brother. Try and get off now if you can.'

'Good-night, Pa.'

The door creaked. He was gone with the glimmer of his candle. As his door closed, that diabolical downpour redoubled; bubbling and hissing in the drains; audibly soaking into a rotting wall somewhere. Soon great drops began to descend the chimney and, to cap it all, a mouse began to gnaw with exacerbating persistence somewhere beneath my bed.

Now, if one sound gets on my nerves more than any other it is a mouse at his gnawing. I just cannot endure it. The very idea of that small, furry beast with its wiry little feet and its squeamish, prehensile tail lifts the hair on the back of my neck, and gives me the grues up my spine. Spiders? yes I like spiders and most insects too, but any kind of rodent and I'm off.

Hurriedly I got out and, donning my dressing-gown and slippers, drew back the curtain and looked out into the black torrent of the night.

At first I saw nothing but the rain cascading from the grass-grown gutter above the window. Then I became aware of the dim luminosity of the flickering street-lamp across the road and at last of what it revealed. A rough-looking man, a sailor by his peaked cap and saturated jersey, was clutching at the posts of Mrs Grintforth's gate, and swaying boozily to and fro. The peak of his cap covered his eyes, but something entirely horrid had me convinced that they were staring with piercing intensity straight into mine. With a sharp gasp of utter terror I let the curtain fall and, turning back, searched wildly for the matches. Having found them, I lit the candle with trembling fingers.

Victor was sitting straight up in bed, his face frozen with fear. 'Sorry,' I said. 'Did I wake you up?' What kept my voice steady, I cannot tell you.

'If you did, Hubert, then I'm bloody glad you did, that's all I can say. Bugger me black, what a nightmare!'

'You've been having one of your specials, then?'

'And how! Look; I'm dripping with sweat!' He turned his head with slow reluctance towards the door. 'I dreamt,' he said in a hoarse whisper, 'that somebody was creeping up the stairs. An appalling ruffian — a sort of ghastly criminal.'

My eyes moved, but to the window, not the door. I had a momentary sense of our being besieged by an immensely malevolent force; something that had been rejected with loathing by all four elements, a true wanderer in limbo. I got Victor back to sleep soon enough. His nerves were made of good sound old stuff. Before blowing out the light I risked another peep behind the curtain. He was gone. The rain still fell in sheets. As far as my sight could pierce, I glared rather dementedly up and down that detestably banal road. But he really had gone, and in what manner I hesitated even to consider; nor who he was or — infinitely worse — what.

Mice had become an irrelevance, a triviality. Flinging off my dressing-gown, I plunged between the carbolic sheets and converted myself into a mummy.

5

In the Thicket

Turning right into Bath Road towards the Thicket, you passed
on your right hand the houses of such magnates as the
Stuchburys, the Cochrans and the Cleaver-Stills, with their
winding drives, and brilliant beds of flowers shaded by the
arching branches of well-grown trees, which included at least
one of those Victorian 'musts', a Cedar of Lebanon.

Then beyond them came the old Pond House at the other
side of the road, pondless now and providing a forecourt for
char-a-bancs instead of refreshment for horses. A further few
hundred yards brought you to the steep declivity of Punt Hill,
and then came a narrow foot-path branching away southward
to the hamlet of Tittle Row.

We knew it as Dick Turpin's Lane, because of the region's
history of highwaymen and footpads, and the Lane's own
notorious air. In days gone by, stage-coachloads rumbled
across Maidenhead Thicket with passengers up from the west
country, who counted themselves lucky to be spared the dread
summons to 'Stand and deliver!' snapped out from a masked
visage behind a pair of barkers, half obscured by mist and the
steam of a horse's breath.

This Lane, ennobled by close-growing wytch-elms, skirted
the gardens of more grand houses where, in summer, croquet
and tennis were played by elderly gentlemen, with dark socks
between white canvas shoes and half-masted white flannel
trousers, and ladies, smartly dowdy, who let out shrill cries of
congratulations or commiseration straight out of Angela Brazil.

As the lane curved leftwards, withdrawing from inhabited
country, the trees thickened, the silence deepened and
narrower shrank the path. The Thicket then announced its
proximity, with clumps of bracken and patches of rabbit-

gnawed turf, springy and soft, pleasing to foot and eye as it was before myxomatosis turned it to tatty scrub.

And at that point, rigid and grim amid the dynamic tangle of undergrowth, appeared the pump, just as if it had, that second, taken two paces forward to confront us.

It was, in all probability, one of those many pumps Beau Nash is said to have persuaded local gentry to erect the length of Bath Road, so that summer visitors to his City should be enabled to arrive clean and tidy from their long and often perilous journey. A similar pump stands near Castle Hill to this day.

Rose was not enamoured of the spot and didn't mind saying so. She said it was spooky and made her think of dead 'uns. To us it was 'simpatico'. A small clearing let the field flowers flood in from the Altwood side. Clovers, vetches, corn-flowers and poppies made a Sabine raid in reverse upon the crude, rank maleness of nettle, perennial mercury and dog-wood. At the height of summer song-birds had gone silent. Only wood-pigeons accentuated the hush with their amorous 'demand et reponse'.

As for the pump, flaking and corroding into ruin, its handle rusting into total immobility, we treated the old thing with scant respect. We climbed upon it, posed upon it as statues, employed it as a mark for whatever weapon accompanied us on our picnic — airgun or catapult — until one hot day, cloudy and limp, with the festering effluvia of a stink-horn on the air, Renee invented the game of posthumously eavesdropping upon the councils of Dick Turpin and his confederate, Tom King. It was the circulation of air within the wide cylindrical tube that, having applied one ear to the spout, one interpreted as murderous threats, plots and plans laid by the two arch-villains. There were lots of 'Gad's Lifes!' 'Ecods!' and 'Stap me Bodies!' There were times when invention was brilliant, others when inspiration failed miserably and dried up, Rose sat there disapprovingly, her Christian Novel in one hand, a ginger-nut in the other, emitting sighs of resignation and occasionally shuddering in an irritatingly melodramatic manner. She just wouldn't or couldn't like that old pump, though we grew fonder of it as the years passed by. It became a kind of inanimate comic...a silly old iron buffoon. In fact we made a cult of it. Renee went so far as to attach a large bunch of sweet-peas to its handle three years running, and had a good deal of good fortune at that time, winning the junior high-diving championship for the County twice in succession, and having a rather good flower painting in gouache accepted by the local museum. A bond of loyalty grew up between us and our ancient bit of hardware.

Amid the dynamic tangle of undergrowth . . . at Maidenhead Thicket, in the late 1920s.

Six years had elapsed: Rose had been five years wed to a nice young Somerset farmer when she might, but for the fact of her consequent withdrawal from our lives, have had the last laugh.

The morning was white and dark-sepia with frost and dead wood. Weedy prongs and spikes punctuated the fallows, gauzy with spiders' webs. Rooks flew low to the ground like blots of indian ink against the light grey and pinkish sky. Plovers circled slowly, flapping wide, oriental wings and mewing miserably.

We came whirring into Dick Turpin's Lane, warmly scarfed and gloved, equipped now with bicycles. Renee's was a three-speed Raleigh as was my friend Billy Franklin's. Victor and I straddled Pilots: wretched local products, equine freaks — despised by all, pitied by none. I quite understood what made our schoolfellows make a laughing stock of our bastardly bikes, averring that their makers, Hickling and Co, assembled their products out of reconditioned and horribly obviously disparate bits. Every time I mounted mine I recalled one of those wretched nags on my uncle's farm at Mulbarton; short in the leg, tubular and slack in the barrel, woefully hammerheaded and utterly stupid, called Creamy. Even the village idiot would hang out his teeth and guffaw at the thing. I found it in my heart to forgive the chaps but not the smart, straw-hatted Mr Farr at the yellow-painted shop in Queen Street, who had so blindly sold them to Pa with a fluent fount of blarney that would have done credit to an Irish son of a gipsy woman and an Arab vendor of filthy picture post-cards.

I came to a stop with bellows to mend from the effort of keeping up with Franklin's velocepedian blood-stock. Victor, swept along by Renee's iron arms and legs, had reached the Thicket already. Through the bare branches they were now to be seen urging us on with heroic gestures.

I realized we had never been this way at this particular time of the year, and looking around, was taken by its wintry charm. There stood the pump, enigmatic as ever, twice as solid and strong, against the gently pastelled tints of frost and pearly sky, as it had shown itself in summer, over-shadowed by bosky foliage, held in the hypnosis of a somnolent summer afternoon. Even its handle had acquired an irresistibly arresting authority.

I cast my plebeian grid-iron into the bushes. Franklin carefully stood his by a tree. He was a neat, dapper lad, faultlessly dressed and rather handsome, the only son of a widowed Captain in the Merchant Navy. He turned upon me his charming but rather pansy smile. 'Well,' he said with irritating patronage, 'Let's see this wonderful antique of yours,

We came whirring into Dick Turpin's Lane . . . Victor and I
straddled Pilots: wretched local products, equine freaks —
tubular and slack in the barrel.

then'. Annoyed by his tone I turned and led the way between wytch-elm suckers and brambles.

There it stood as if alive. And why not indeed? Had we not over a period of six or seven years imbued it with a spirit, as a little girl does with her doll? I turned to Franklin to see what impression it was making upon him with its cloak of rusty scales, its grotesquely shaped head and its oracular spout.

Imagine my dismay at seeing a deathly pallor overspread his face and a wildness in his eye, which I took momentarily as the initial stages of some sort of a fit or seizure. I knew he was supposed to be of a delicate constitution, and how the beaks were easy in their treatment of him. Supposing he were to collapse on me now in this solitary place where not even a milk-cart passed by. My heart in my mouth, I watched his arms go out as if to ward off something that threatened, something that brought an expression of loathing to his milk-white face. I said in a trembling ghost of my own voice, 'Billy, what's up? What on earth is it?'

Without a word he began a crab-like, sideways retreat back towards the lane, his gaze in terrified fixation upon the pump. It looked as if he could just about keep to his legs and no more.

By this time I was on the edge of the horrors myself. I'd not breakfasted because of a mild digestive upset. My stomach now seemed on the point of eating itself alive with its own acids.

I shouted, 'Billy, for God's sake...!' But when at last he reached the Lane, he ignored me and sank, regardless of damage to his precious pants, upon the frosty ground, his back against a tree and his head in his hands. That weird retreat of his, his horror-filled eyes, that eerie doddering of his legs, had sent a freezing finger up my spine, and I swear that, returning my glance to that old, familiar pump, I could well have given way to a belief of its having, in one split second, reassumed its normal appearance from something quite radically different. Physically and mentally windy, I took off with a smothered yell of panic fear, tripping in brambles, my cheeks stung by the shrivelled but quite sufficiently efficient nettles, my ears flicked wickedly by the wytch elm shoots. I didn't stop until my feet hit the footpath.

Victor and Renee were nowhere in sight. The opulent houses of the croquet-playing Poshocracy had a discouragingly distant look. Smoke from their tall chimneys fountained perpendicularly in the still, cold air, spreading out high up into feathery vanishing plumes. Like a tonic, the shrill song of a robin rang out in the bushes, recalling that long-distant morning when Miss Mayne had entrusted Muriel to my small and inky hands.

I now regarded Franklin with pitying distaste, cursing him inwardly for an hysterical effeminate, a wet blanket on a fine, stimulating day. He had, I noted, stopped his trembling and was rising slowly to his feet, his eyes still upon the pump but with relief within them. For me every detail of this familiar scene had returned to such sweet normality that, given less schoolboy self-consciousness, I might have burst into raucous song — something changeing-roomish and rude; just to shock the rather tender susceptibilities of Billy Franklin. Besides, Victor and Renee would be by now at Pinkney's Green, chancing sodden feet on the cat-ice.

I gave the stupid boy a roughish nudge. 'Come on, old chap,' I said. 'Don't play the giddy goat for Heaven's sake. Trying to turn our old pump into something evil...! Pull yourself together. This is the way girls behave.'

Slowly he looked up, revealing a still pale but now surprisingly calm face, bearing a tinge of what I can only describe as resignation. 'I'm not trying anything of the sort,' he declared. 'It is an evil thing, your old pump and I bet I'm not the only one to say so. It ought to be chopped down and burnt, that's what I say. Damn you and your pump! Seeing is believing, and if you saw nothing then — then good luck to you!'

'But what on earth did you see, Billy, to make you lose your pluck like that? Tell me and get the thing off your chest!'

His look of contempt for my lack of sensitivity was killing.

'I'll tell you nothing, my brave soldier, except to look out it doesn't happen to you one of these fine frosty mornings — specially if you persist in mooching about in rotten places like this one. Other things can get at you just as easily as a damned pump. You look out, that's all!'

'Other things? What do you mean, other things? I've never heard such a load of silly old tripe. Unhealthy, that's what you are...right down unhealthy.'

He wrenched his bicycle round and prepared to mount. Anger with me had replaced his fear. I began to see what had so often got on my nerves in my dealings with him. Always some over-intense emotion somewhere in the background, some little scheme for making himself interesting. 'Go off, then, and try your piddling games on some other sucker,' I snapped, 'I wish I'd brought old Timberlake along instead of you. At least we'd have had a bit of fun with our pump. Being with you is sometimes like being with a dog that keeps on looking around the room when you're alone with it. You're beastly spooky, that's what you are.'

He threw a leg over his bike. 'That's you to a T, Hubert. That fiendish little ruffian is right up your street. You're two of a kind. Rowdy, insensitive brutes.' The look of contempt returned to his face. 'I don't know why I ever came to bother with you, dashed if I do.'

'To Hell!' I snapped. 'To hear you talk one would take you for a bloody girl. Old Timbers is worth a dozen of your sort.'

Without another word he pedalled off in his sluggish, big-bummed way. He really needed that Sturmey-Archer three-speed gear.

I hung about rather aimlessly after he'd gone, muttering, 'like a tart — like a bloomin' little tart!' Then I stopped fuming, to savour the agreeably regained tranquillity of the place. The smoking chimneys, the robin's shrilling, the bitter-sweet frosty tang of the air. If evil there had been, it had slunk off with Franklin, and there was no doubt of our old pump's return to normality. I looked at it with renewed affection as I pulled my eccentric mount from the bushes. There was even a familiar pleasure about its clumsy stance. I wouldn't have changed places with a gink like Franklin for all the Raleighs in the world, three-speed and all. 'Happy Christmas to the silly sod,' I muttered, 'and to his bogey-men as well!'

And when I reached the pond at Pinkney's Green, with its tall thin rushes, it was to find that Renee had gone in over the top of her drawers. Between cold, discomfort and fury she was in a state better imagined than described. For a while we rolled about in mirth on the fine turf. In the end we advised her to take them off and tuck them in her pocket. She managed very well by tucking the front of her skirt between her legs, and riding with her knees clasped tightly together.

It was the new year before I saw Billy again. He wore an ordinary tweed cap rather flashily on one side. A very wide crepe band encircled his arm. He was emerging from Breakspears' the Chemists. The look he gave me as I stopped was strange — a sort of continuation of the contemptuous one with which he had left me at the pump; but now there seemed to be something additional to it. A touch of lugubrious triumph perhaps.

'Very sorry to hear about your father,' I said with some awkwardness. 'A—a terrible thing to happen at such a season.'

At once I was aware of the clergyman-like tone of my voice and was ashamed. Franklin's visage filled with irony.

'Thanks,' he almost sneered. 'And for the wreath and kind condolences.'

I blushed scarlet with indignation and no little anger at his sarcasm. Our friendship had never been of that intimate kind that calls for floral tributes and conventional condolences, but I stuck to my guns. He had good enough reason to feel bitterness. One is not orphaned more than once in one's life, and that rakish tweed cap had a strong touch of pathos. So I blundered on with an attempt at clumsy kindness! 'It was off Flamborough Head, wasn't it, old chap?' 'Yes,' he replied in a tone suggesting that I had certainly blown up the fatal storms myself. 'The ship went down with all hands. Every poor son of a bitch.'

'Oh,' I said, suddenly eager to get as far as possible from that malicious face under the unfamiliar and, I considered now, quite common flat cloth cap.

'There was one exception,' he abruptly shot at me. 'Mr Cradock, the first officer. He went overboard un-noticed just a few hours out of Tampico.'

'How awful. Poor devil. Like some kind of warning.'

His expression gained in malice. 'You might say that. Indeed YOU would!'

Unable any longer to meet those cold eyes of his, I looked away up Kings Street towards the Railway Station. I was cutting prayers in order to meet Muriel off her train; risking a beating. Guilt and desire already confused me, and now it began to snow again.

'And do you know what?' His tone had assumed an unwarrantable censoriousness. Rotten with nerves, I reacted sharply. How dared this ordinarily sheepish boy take such a tone with me?

'Well, what?'

'It was him I saw down there in the Lane.'

'What?'

'Old Cradock — large as life and twice as nasty. So much for your dear, friendly bloody old pump! Shakes you a bit, does it? Hope it doesn't put you off it for life.'

He let out a little snigger as he opened his packet from Breakspears. Now he popped a cough lozenge between his lips and gave it a suck or two. 'I'm going to Rio de Janeiro to live with my old Spanish aunt,' he said. 'She's an old tartar, I'm told, but rich as Uncle Croesus. She'll keep me in chocolate-creams until the time comes for her to cough up my boodle. Good-bye, Hubert: I'll write to you one of these fine days — that is if old Cradock isn't waiting for me off Tampico.'

He was gone into the thick, feathery snow, swallowed up in an instant.

Muriel wasn't on her train. Thickly encrusted with the now mercilessly driving snow, I battled my way up the steep curve of Shoppenhangers Road. I had risked Mr Brooke's torture-twig for nothing and Franklin's weird story now tinged my day like the after-effect of an evil dream.

I never saw him or heard from him again. He might have joined Mr Cradock down among the dead men off Tampico.

There came over me a human snow-man, staggering through the school gateway, a most uncanny thought. To actually see a ghost must be ghastly enough as an experience. But was it a much healthier feeling to have seen another person seeing one? I wouldn't have been in Billy's shoes as he went 'rolling down to Rio!'

And that is why, two and a half years later, after a delicious lunch of shoulder of lamb, exquisitely tiny sprouts and crisp roasted potatoes in Mrs Grintforth's unexpectedly comfortable dining-room, I stood at the window with ineffable relief, watching my sailor-man, as real as real could be, tacking and feather-stitching along the gutter at closing time, coughing and spitting over a pipe as black as a factory chimney, mumbling and cursing to himself. I blessed him for his sordid reality. Just an ordinary old local drunk, whose name I later discovered to be Josh Bagot.

6

Queen Anne Schooldays

I would gladly have become her slave but for her instantly
becoming mine. Soon, I'm afraid, I came to take her rather for
granted, with the natural selfishness of the schoolboy. She
would fetch and carry for me and I would let her. There were
times, too, when I forgot her and turned back to natural boyish
aggression. Teddy Norkett would be the one to halt the
movement towards civilization Muriel had started. A trip, a
barge and we were away: rolling and struggling on the polished
floor of the Playroom; punching away at each other's ribs,
infighting savagely. Sometimes weapons were employed and
that was Norkett's fault. I preferred straight fisticuffs, but he
rejoiced in the use of rather nasty battle devices such as large
pebbles knotted in a handerkerchief, or a faggot of bramble
cuttings from the rubbish-heap. He fought with passion and
ruthlessness, with open nostrils and a wild look in his eyes that
I found disturbing. Fortunately, he was a bit of a natural
coward and it was usually enough if I turned my skinny but
very strong arms into a pair of pneumatic drills, battering my
way through the pain-barrier of his superior reach, to hammer
away like the clappers until he simply turned tail, his highland
blood effectively cooled. Once or twice I got a very strong
feeling that Miss Mayne would be pretty happy to be well rid
of us; that it was high time we were moving on.

The truth was that I was running the last course of childish
innocence, a course strewn with all the flowers of early spring,
then of summer and finally of autumn. From that first robin's
glad trill to the early, remote mystery of the first cuckoo's call
from Grenfell Park I was in Heaven. Snow-drops, crocuses,
then hyacinths and jonquils, and at length the incomparable

perfume of ox-eyed narcissus were in the garden, mingling with freshly turned mould and the coarse, thick texture of Mr Rickett's barrow-loads of steaming horse manure.

Every morning we met upon the stairs; she coming up with the train-children, I coming down from prayers. With a half-movement which stopped just short of being a caress, we allowed the throng of children to separate us until play-time.

I have a suspicion that Miss Mayne began, at a certain stage of our juvenile courtship, to entertain doubts as to the wisdom of permitting it to remain so very exclusive. Indeed, one morning in the little library adjoining the play-room, she did make the suggestion that it might be nice for us to join in the games with the others. Muriel's open-eyed alarm, a quick blanching of her cheeks, brought the head-mistress up in her tracks.

'No, really, Miss Mayne! I'll be all right with Hubert — really I will!'

'And what about Hubert?' She stamped my copy of *The Charcoal Burners*. 'Don't your friends appeal to you any longer?'

'Not really, Miss Mayne. They seem to want to quarrel all the time. The boys want to fight and we're getting a bit big for that — at least here. It's really much nicer talking to Muriel. We seem to like the same things. Books and things — you know — flowers...that sort of thing.'

'Yes, I know,' said Miss Mayne rather forlornly. 'Ah, well, we'll be stopping play-room fire next week and going out into the garden in our coats if it's fine. You'll like that I'm sure. It will do us all good, won't it?'

'Oh, yes!' Muriel looked relieved as she seized her indigo covered copy of *Little Black Mingo*. 'Oh, yes, that will be lovely!'

'I wish,' she murmured as we crossed the play-room, 'We could play over at the Big School. It's all so beautiful and mysterious under the rhododendrons. And the Fir-Walk....Don't you adore it? The trees always seem to be singing something sad and lovely!'

'It's a bit smelly though, the old Fir-Walk. It suits me alright when it's nice and blowy. The Council School kids dump their cargoes behind the little bush along the wall. Pooh!'

We were last as usual to go up. Behind the heavy curtain at the main door, she put her elegant little hand in mine and gave me her cool little kiss.

And that was the first and only time anybody sought to interfere between us. That is until Lucy Wentworth came among us; springing like an over-eager actress from the wings. But that was much later on in the summer, with cherries hanging by the wall, the heavy scent of roses everywhere and black, red and white currants trailing their ropes across the kitchen garden paths, and almost the most delicious of all, the thick but delicate aroma of pinks — Mrs Simpkin's pinks, raised originally by a work-house master from Slough and named after his wife. Mr Ricketts had made a long, broad border of them at the extremity of the vegetable patch, just where they caught the hot afternoon sun and the gentle south-westerly breeze. Let me but catch that same fragrance, be it but for a second, and I am back there as if by magic carpet: listening to my first girl-friends's sweet, untidy, delicious chatter; revelling in the charming originality of her dress; in her very personal and private chic. And don't run away with the idea that I claim any greater powers of conversation than she herself possessed. We just gibbered and trilled away like a pair of young birds....not caged love-birds, you understand. More like larks. Shakespeare's larks at Heaven's Gate.

How did the Devil come? — When first attack? queried Sir John Betjeman in his poem *Norfolk*. I will relate how he came to me and describe his mode of assault.

He came with a hum and a flicker and a flutter through a small rectangular aperture behind the darkened auditorium of the Bridge Street Picture Palace in the form of an ever-widening beam of light, curdled with tobacco-smoke, dancing with a million moths and motes. Over the heads of me and my fellow spectators he shot, finally to strike and spread himself upon an immense silver screen where, albeit amongst other marvels, he showed me SIN! Not to the sounds of mighty organs or to breast-shaking trumpets and sackbuts intoning the *Dies Irae*, but to the tinkling of a piano running a musically emotional gamut between the *Laughing Vamp* and *Hearts and Flowers*.

Mind you, I was nearly nine years old, and had been a cinema-goer for some three years before I apprehended the sinfulness of it all. Those tiresome wrestling matches between fiercely famished-looking men with straggley moustaches and shrinking ladies in negligée gowns, boudoir-caps massively heaving their embonpoint....Suddenly they were not tiresome any more but wildly and intensely disturbing and exciting. Sleeves were ripped off, dresses torn at the shoulder; ravaged ladies were left weeping like fountains on sofas. I have a notion that beds were not allowed just yet. Naturally what happened between the wrestling and the abandonment of the weeper was a complete blank to me, but that dreadful little worm, the erotic nerve, was awakened, and juvenile sadism set in with a vengeance! Keystone Cops and their chases took a diminishing part in my enjoyment of the shadow show; cowboys and indians shrank to small potatoes. Serial cliff-hangers took on a dreary sameness. I began to look around my little friends for potential victims of my prurient sadism. I was agog for victims — in vain, alas. Moreover there was Muriel, my good angel, and she represented for me the principal of sacred as opposed to profane love, and, I felt, always would.

Then one summer afternoon on the echoing stairs, I saw Lucy Wentworth and bang went my innocence. I was almost aware of the fluttering of its wings in its flight.

Lucy's auburn curls were unkempt but wonderfully glossy; her clothes were shabby but strikingly picturesque and gipsyish, and withal she had handsomely aristocratic features and hands which, though large and strong, were beautifully shaped and capable. Without having spent much time in her company I had been made luridly familiar with the facts of her home-life and her father's rather dubious reputation. He was an artist for a start, and one knew the kind of individuals they were. Then he drank like a fish, and moreover, had a woman living with him at his house out at Holyport, whom he was said to paint in the altogether. This house of his was enormous and a by-word for shabby neglect, reprehensible extravagance, dissipated company and dirt. Orgies were mentioned. All these things I learned from the lips of my elders and better. A little pitcher's proverbially elongated ears marvellously adjust their tuning the second a jolly gossip reduces itself to strangled whispering. But the devil struck again; this time using the busy tongue of Mrs Egbert from across the Avenue.

'That poor little daughter too,' she commented in her rather pleasantly rusty voice. 'Did you ever see the like of her? Why those awful knitted dresses scarcely hang on her, do they? I always feel when I see her that I want to tear them from her shoulders and dress her really prettily. She's such a charming little thing....'

That was all I needed. There whizzed through my head a violent gallopado of those persecuted women of the silver screen and their ravaged frocks, their panting bosoms and collapsing hairdos.

As if by some fatal telepathy that morning upon the stairs, Lucy turned and smiled entrancingly. It was all I needed. Up the stairs I galloped, overtook her at her form-room door and incontinently jerked a handful of pea-green knitwear from her shoulder, revealing white, large-pored skin, and causing a fall of pins, and a parting of slovenly stitching and cobbling.

Terror at what I had done brought up my hand, to parry, slap or scratch. Imagine my amazement to see the girl calmly produce a huge safety-pin from somewhere and, proceeding deftly to repair the damage I had wrought, smile upon me in a manner which I can only describe as roguish, and which invited me in no uncertain terms to repeat the performance at any time I cared to.

Embarassed by this charming complaisance, I looked dazedly around. My dramatic coup de cinema seemed to have passed unnoticed — or so I thought.

I was mistaken. On the following day Miss Gould drew up the cast for the end-of-term play, to take place in the garden of the Big School. It was the Arthurian story of Gareth and Lynette. I wasn't too pleased to be chosen as Gareth, but was shaken to the marrows when I heard Muriel decline with extraordinary resolution the part of Lynette. Her friend, Brenda, accepted with glee the role of the haughty Lady Lyoness and I shuddered. So my aimiable assault on Lucy had got around after all, and it now fell upon me to endure, not only Muriel's looks of unbearable reproach but, more frighteningly, her friend's more practical and painful demonstrations of hatred and contempt. Neither was on speaking terms with me, but the hatred and vindictiveness of Brenda were accompanied by diverse acts of incredible violence. On stage, when the play finally came to its first performance, she privily kicked at my pasteboard greaves and, after each performance, returning in crocodile formation down the steep steps to Castle Hill, assailed my ears with humiliatingly witty comments upon my character, personal habits and appearance until, between her shrewish aspersions and Muriel's beseeching remonstrances, I shrank from both Brenda's venom and savagery (my ankles were black and blue and my buttocks one great ache from her constant kneeings), and Muriel's tender forgiveness in about equal proportions 'Please don't, dear — please, please don't!' Muriel would implore in agony. And with a half-glance back I would hate her as much as I hated her friend and champion.

'My Gracious!' the latter would spit 'Just fancy having to call it Fair Knight — that!' Then she kicked me again.

That same afternoon, in perverse desperation, and without the slightest desire for it, I tried my tricks on with Lucy once more.

The slap she returned rattled my skull like a bag full of beans, and jarred every tooth in my jaws.

'Little swine!' she snapped, and turned away with a toss of her glossy, auburn curls. Then she went around whispering in the ears of the rest, making of me a jest and a by-word.

Forlornly I looked around for Muriel, and comfort for my shattered ego. Her beautiful oblique eyes had narrowed; her lips had a mocking downwards twist at the corners. She just looked at me. The entire world was leagued against me and all had gone sour. I had begun to learn about women. The Devil had come.

She was getting into the dicky seat of a bull-nosed Morris: Julia was the girl next door, who helped us raise the ghost of Canon Drummond.

The surviving memories I have of that last breaking-up day at Queen Anne are of Muriel, seemingly as merry as a grig, passing with sedate cheerfulness the window where old Mr Waizeneker sat repairing his watches and clocks. She looked not to have a care or regret in the world, and Dennis Brierly, a stuck-up son of a bitch, was carrying her books with a look of triumph on his smug, clever, mathematician's face. I could have punched it.

I watched Lucy too. She was getting into the dicky-seat of a quite ordinary bull-nosed Morris Cowley in the front seat of which sat, very upright, a staid looking couple who might have been a bank-clerk and his wife out for a 'spin.'

I was soon heartened. Renee and her many friends, Victor and his, even Teddy Norkett, rallied round. The train-children were not really very popular. Their immunity from morning prayers was generally resented, as was their privilege — for so we saw it — of getting off early in the afternoon to catch their train.

Renee summed the whole thing up in a few words. 'It's jolly nice to see you off that little fool's apron-strings,' she said. 'You didn't cut a very pretty figure, you know.'

It didn't sound very nice but she meant well, I supposed.

In St Marks Road we met Wally Bidwell, the local simpleton, pushing his ruined little old pram, busy as usual, collecting the droppings of horses which were at that time pretty plentiful. Just an old kitchen shovel he had to fill his gim-crack vehicle. In place of a brush he made out with his long and bony fingers. As we passed by, he picked up a golden-brown apple of dung from his pram and pelted us affectionately. He was a sweet-natured chap, and his projectile was intended as a gesture, similar to an invitation to a game of snow-balls. Tall as a tree, he was; black-eyed, hair cropped almost to the scalp, and his mouth like the Mersey tunnel. Between his fat lips shone teeth as white as snow, widely spaced and fierce, while his thick, black eye-brows met in a bunchy knot at the bridge of his nose. Yet, and we fully realized this, given sanity, a tongue to speak with and ears to hear, he might have been a handsome fellow.

'Hallo, Wally,' called Renee, and threw him one of her toffees.

'Ugh — Ugh — Ugh!' he replied, picked it from the road and popped it straight into his poor, dumb mouth. He must, I supposed, have got used to the taste of horse-manure by now. All the same, I was always upset at the sight of those short knickers on the legs of a young man of at least six foot four.

I soon forgot Muriel. We had, after all, lived the bits of life we spent in each others' company entirely in the school house and grounds. In those times of limited transport, we travelled mostly upon our feet, and it was almost eight miles to Cygnet Green.

7

Away from Queen Street

By Monday's first post came a letter from Mooghie. I was first down, alone in the dining-room where Mrs Grintforth had lit a small fire in the grate, for the weather had turned unpleasantly cold.

Mooghie's letter was moving and at the same time disconcerting, its discreet warmth thinly cloaking a depth of passion that brought a lump to my throat and set my heart beating fast and painfully. Gone was the slight and lovesome aimlessness of her chatter. The words she had put down on these six pages were fraught with a clarity and candour that hit me straight where I lived. For two pins I could have gone down and planked my return fare in front of the booking-clerk. Alas, my generation was conditioned to respect for commonsense and parental authority and, moreover, kept pretty short of funds.

The latter consideration was, for once, nugatory because, on dropping me off at Cygnet Green Halt that Saturday morning Doctor Campbell had asked me point-blank how much holiday money I was allowed and, when told five bob, had blown out his ruddy cheeks, ejaculated 'My God' and jerked a bank-note from his note-case.

'There, now you've got five quid!' he growled, 'And be sure you spend it on rubbish and pleasure and a jolly good blow-out for the youngsters. Now don't you forget, old son, have a good old pow-wow with your father about what we discussed last night. I hope he's less starchy about it than he was with me on the telephone. Tell him I'll be in touch with him as soon as he returns. Perhaps I'll find him in a better mood. He didn't seem all that keen on you spending the night with us....Odd.'

'It's only his way,' I replied uncomfortably.

'Oh, well....' he smiled at me cheerfully. 'We'll bring him round, laddie. I can't see him resisting Mooghie for long. Happy vacation to you all — cheerio!' and off he shot, smooth as velvet in his black and yellow Daimler sports coupé, leaving me standing by the foot-bridge with a lovely, silky, old-fashioned fiver fluttering between my fingers, and with the scent in my nostrils from the red and white speckled moss-rose Mrs Campbell had placed in my buttonhole. I had the scene fresh as paint upon my mind's eye. That lovely pair waving me farewell; incredible in their house-gowns, one azure, the other old rose. Behind them their ivy-clad house sat handsome and comfortable in a light gauze of sun-shot mist, and I could clearly perceive the informally civilized comforts of the pagoda-roofed verandah, with the fresh white cloth of the breakfast table, an enormous hammock, and Mooghie's guitar stretched across a French Colonial basketchair. In the far distance Cliveden Woods rode high over the morning mists like a visition of Laputa.

Now, from Mrs Grintforth's kitchen wafted a delicious pleasance of eggs and bacon and coffee. Unfortunately we were in for — as well as a really good breakfast — a decidedly nasty shock. On this dour Lowestoft morning of grey brick, furtive front garden shrubs and faintly luminous light purple sky I had scarcely anticipated lounging upon the beach. At best, a stroll to the Harbour, a visit to the *Godetia*, the guardian frigate of the fisheries and perchance, afterwards, hot coffee in a tea-room or ice-cream parlour somewhere along the rather tatty esplanade. With astonishment I saw Pa enter wearing, not his light-brown sports jacket and flannels, but the formal garb of the day before. We were all even more shocked to see Ma come in wearing her Mrs Merrick cloche. More, because Pa was a naturally formal person, and this didn't look good at all. I felt jelly under the floor. I smelt mischief. A glance at Victor confirmed my unease. His intelligent eyes were brimming with mistrust. Neither was Pa's expression any more reassuring. There was strain there; anxiety and quite pitiable vulnerability. Yet, even while I sympathized with his obvious unhappiness, my wretchedly perverse mind was at one of its nastier little games. Try as I might to identify myself with him in whatever was troubling him; to take his side against the world if necessary (which, in fact, I would have with both fists flying), I was utterly unable to prevent there leaping to my mind's eye a grotesquely symbolic image, worthy of Salvador Dali himslf. My father and his agony of anxiety and tension vanished, to be replaced by the vision of a whelk, untimely ripped from its shell, like Macduff from his mother's womb, and shuddering, tragically naked in a callously unfamiliar world.

But his spirit was all alive. 'For God's sake,' he exclaimed testily, 'take that hat off while you eat your breakfast. It looks downright indecent. We're not on the train to Norwich yet!'

'Norwich?' snapped Victor. 'Why are you going to Norwich?'

'We've got a little business with your Uncle Ted.'

'That' said Pa in sour imitation of his in-law's chapel-haunting jargon, 'is why we girt up our loins, as you see!

Ma ignored this primly. 'Your grandma is coming to take care of you while we're gone. She — '

'What, old gritty Grandma?' Victor exploded.

'Really — '

'The old bald battle-axe herself.' Pa managed the sad ghost of a smile. 'The Lord be with you, lads.' He turned a withering look on Ma. 'And I tell you this.....If Hubert were not here I would not leave them in the care of that old besom for one second — not for a split atom of a second. And for two pins I'd chuck the whole project this minute. So look out, that's all!'

I blinked. Never before in my recollection had Pa uttered a single word expressing genuine confidence in me. Even high marks or brilliant commendations from my examiners at the Royal College of Music did not fail to fill his cannister with morbid qualms about the next one. Every talent I had he tended to denigrate by a force of habit induced by my first terrible school report. He had never recovered from that. He placed these talents of mine — and God knows they were unimportant enough — side by with my mathematical ineptitude and my sad lack of gamesmanship. Proficiency at games, he would insist, betokened character and spunk, and at maths a sound, well-balanced, logical mind. I really suppose it never entered his mind that music has its own system of mathematics, built-in. It was just the same with my fencing, at which I was more than proficient. Even having been inspired to take it up by the exploits of the great Lord Desborough cut no ice with old Pa. It was bayonets, not knitting-needles, these days, he firmly declared and, with a glance at his souvenir of Mother Russia, I would withdraw in shame from further argument.

What worry and trouble was in the wind now? What had robbed his face of its customary neat, taut lines, leaving a quite unfamiliar slackness around his jaws? What predicament awaited him in Norwich?

'We could very well have done without her.' I complained.

'You must have somebody responsible to look after you,' Ma replied.

'But why her? Why grandma? We're more likely to find ourselves looking after her.'

'I can't have you playing all alone on the beach — '

'Playing — ? On the beach — ? I'm almost seventeen — remember?'

She turned to Pa for support, but Pa, with half-open mouth and up-turned El Greco eyes was lost to this world in a condition of dumb misery. He seemed to be looking Heavenwards and finding Hell instead.

The parents had departed. Grandma had arrived. She had taken the tram from the station, of course. Though well able to afford the taxi-fare, she would as soon have mounted the Black Maria as yield to such an extravagance. She was a little old lady with steely grey eyes and brows sharply arched. She put one in mind of a stern little owl, perpetually amazed at the extent of the world's sinning. On her scant grey locks, eked out by an unpleasant bit of grizzly material she called her rat, was pinned a beaver bonnet of brown, and her top-coat was cylindrical in shape and much adorned with convoluted designs of black braid and pearl buttons.

By now the wind had got up more briskly. It was certainly no weather for the beach, but what must this perverse old lady do but drag us off to the most desolate tract of shingle between South and Claremont piers, overlooked by a row of twisted ocean deities, sculpted in so badly weathered a stone as to be almost completely shapeless. Here a broken trident and a dolphin's tail, there a flattened face with a single moustachio miraculously spared by the flensing gales and driving sleet of mid-winter, or a mermaid's frost-pitted breast: a fossilized melon embedded in the general gallimaufry of marine mythology.

Minutely directed, we placed her deck-chair close to an ugly beach-revétement, shrouded her meagre form in a heavy magenta rug all made up of knitted squares sewn together, then stood back to watch her transfix the bowl-shaped bonnet with an extra pin before, delving into her lumpy black hold-all, she produced first a paperbag containing enormous gob-stopping pear drops and secondly a heavy, old-fashioned edition of *The Sorrows of Satan* by Miss Marie Corelli.

We exchanged glances. There was a score or so of people on the strand beside ourselves; macintoshed, keeping themselves and their offspring warm with ball- and dog-play, dodging the shallow surge of the waves, doing their best to keep up their spirits with unconvincing cries of excitement. Others, shapelessly fuddled and veiled, bent searching for amber along the tide-line. Punch and Judy remained enshrouded, their proprietor, no doubt, enjoying a drop of something wet and warm at his digs, his swozzle-stick dry in his pocket, and dreaming of prosperous bottlings whenever the weather should consent to break. The al fresco stage, also cloaked in its wet-weather garments, resembled a defunct organ awaiting burial.

When we had thus prepared her, we stood back like artists preparing to get to work upon a particularly distasteful subject. Tony was shivering his ears loose, Victor's eyes were taking in every aspect of the horrible little Spartan for some future impersonation and, as for me, I was recalling all the disparaging things she had said of our well-loved native place. How could she, I speculated, unless insane, damn with the faintest praise our beautiful rolling pasture-lands and the bathing-pool at Hurley, fresh with its foamy aeration by the tumbling weir, and yet find positive pleasure here amidst the briny desolation of shingle beach, dark, broken groynes and sluggishly heaving green-grey expanse of ocean? There could be no doubt about it: the old daisy was regaling herself, sniffing at the breeze like an ancient mare about to laugh among the trumpets!

Suddenly she spoke. 'Ent you boys gooing to have a nice paddle while that weather hold?' she demanded with, I was convinced, biting irony. At the very idea of such a proceeding I felt as if my feet had been severed.

'You will forgive me, Grandma,' I remarked, 'if I remind you how very thin our blood is at present. We come from a sunnier clime, you know.'

'Ah, yes, that's soo. The soft and sinful South! That's more bracing in these regions, ent it?'

I began to feel angry. Mooghie's letter was burning a hole in my pocket as was her father's fiver. I looked Grandma straight in her falcon's eye. 'I'm going to get something hot into my brothers' stomachs at once!' I snapped. 'Shall we come back for you in about an hour?'

Deliberately she took out a pear-drop, holding it up like an enormous uncut jewel. 'That take me about twenty minutes to suck through one of these,' she informed me. 'I'll expect you back when I've a-done with three. In the mean-time doon't you goo falling in the Harbour. I doon't want any trouble with your father.' So saying she popped the pear-drop between her lips, instantly imparting to the breeze for a fleeting second a strong flavour of acetone.

'Then I will return for you at exactly three,' I ventured in fatuous jest.

'Answer not the fool according to his folly — umph!' retorted Grandma, opening Miss Corelli's fat volume at the place indicated by a highly religious looking marker. The old faggot didn't even require spectacles for that minute Victorian print!

With a glance at the tide, fast running out and leaving a single bit of splendour to the scene: a silvery streak of whiteness across the weedy strand, I left her with relief to catch up with my young brothers, already climbing the wall to the Esplanade.

Grandma had had eleven children. My grandfather, a Methodist lecturer and lecher — a not uncommon combination — had died, unsurprisingly at the early age of fifty-four. All his offspring had, by marriage or merchandising, done well for themselves — all save Ma, who was said to have married beneath her. Pa they socially despised while personally handling with kid-gloves. All the uncles had contrived to avoid war-service, embraced war-profits and got rich. With true peasant paradox they now turned up their Norfolk noses at us for our relative poverty, simultaneously and rather inconsistently avowing that we were stuck-up, affected and generally lah-di-da. Now, in her declining years, Grandma pilgrimaged from one household to the other and, strange as it may seem, spent most of these holidays with us. Heaven knows why she so honoured and afflicted us, for a cloud of alleged discomforts and displeasures engulfed her from the moment she arrived. Her bed was the only feature that escaped whipping. I should know, for it was mine, I being bundled in with Victor for the extent of her stay.

Rose hated her and jerked the right corner of her mouth towards her right ear every time she opened her lips to extol the charms and beauties of Norwich. I remember how hard we tried to make her admire the Thicket, always in vain. It was too close and hot; there were too many flies; the little paths through the under-brush were too narrow and, when we sat down to our picnic tea, the wasps chose her as their especial victim and assailed her jam sandwich without mercy. The bracken, also, was much too tall and smothering and one could hardly sit down for the rabbits' currants.

It was the same when we introduced her to the olfactory delights of the honeysuckle. She spent the whole time with her small button-nose thrust suspiciously forward, morbidly on the lookout for a stray urchin's turd upon which she might step or as she put it, set her shoe. With the sweetness of honeysuckle in her nostrils she was inhaling an imaginary stink!

The climax came for Rose when, one hazy-dazy afternoon, we came upon an uncommonly fine patch of wild-strawberries in a grassy clearing just off the Henley Road. Now for Rose, the finding of such bounty involved protocol. Slowly, with seemly deliberation we must pick them, and then, leaving a few to ripen further, bring them to her for sharing. This usage was for the simple, honest Rose a process symbolising absolute fairness. It was, as a matter of fact, a lesson I never forgot.

Imagine, then, her sense of outrage at the spectacle of Grandma, fallen suddenly to her knees, scrambling indecently among the frail and fairy-like fruit and flowers, tearing away at the cymes and stripping them one after another as though shelling peas, and, when her palm was over-spilling, shovelling them into her munching lips with all the parched desperation of an aged prospector discovering water, after an all-fours crawl across days of desert.

Rose was done with Grandma. Ma might remonstrate and threaten, Nessie Spindler might try sweet reason, it was all in vain. Grandma was expelled from our picnics and expeditions. I actually saw Pa next day waylay our heroine on her way to Mr Keiller's and, after a sheepish look around them, fold into her hand something which, after an Ascot Sunday session at the Windsor Castle, he might refer to as one as the 'readies'.

But I would not give up. As the years rolled on it became a point of honour that Grandma must and should be brought to confessed admiration for our native territory. It grew, indeed, to obsessive proportions. I tried the historical approach. Standing outside the nice, chaste little Library, shaded by its spreading cedar tree in St Ives Road, just opposite Ives Place with its stucco castellations, I told her about Anne of Cleves and how she had wrested from her new and ferocious Royal husband, for the price of the annulment of their marriage, not only the combined manors of Ives and Bisham, but a good fat pension into the bargain. With a burst of dramatic narrative I abolished Butler's stores, Biggs, the celebrated jeweller, St Mary's Church, the Bear Hotel, in fact the entire townscape, evoking in its place a Tudor pleasance, lost in a world of thicket, ferny brake and sweeping country. Was she fascinated by this inspired tour de force? Did she exhibit the least interest in Henry's impotence, faced with the risk of losing the alliance with John of Cleves against the mighty Catholic countries of France and Spain? A bit older, less pompous, I might well have twigged that what she really desired was to hear of the lecheries and treacheries of the Tudor Court: of torture, blood and beheadings. With discouragement I beheld her wandering gaze, heard her bawdy old gossip's interpolations and, finally noticing in her bag a copy of *The Scandalous History of Maria Monk*, stammered to a halt. At the same time Grandma, clearly regretful at having allowed herself to lapse into bawdry, turned upon Mr E.T. Bigg's beautiful shop — a real slice of Bond Street if ever there was one — the full fury of her reaction.

'All that wicked wealth flaunted in the faces of the poor and needy...! Truly and utterly sinful! Ah, lay not up for yourselves treasures on earth — Umph!'

I thought of Mr Bigg's family and the agreeable parties they gave over the shop, and in the large tree-shaded garden at the back beside the flood-stream. Peggy, Mary and Teddy....I had been at Queen Anne with all three, and was now at County Boys with Teddy. Nice, unassuming people they were with all their prosperity.

With a pointed look at Maria Monk, I goaded Grandma to the cab rank in Station Approach, summoned Mr Rance and handed her in. She looked as tired as I felt. She wanted to object on the score of extravagance, but I was now fourteen and strong with self-imposed disciplines. We were driven home, and she paid up like a good 'un.

It was worse when we took her on the River. The punt-pole made her nervous; I was giving her a shower-bath. Thames valley breezes were not nice and fresh and 'whoolesome' as those of the Norfolk Broads. The idle rich were a constant slap in the face to the poor and lowly, with their motor-launches and champagne and their over-dressed, high-stomached arrogance. Grandma was on good form that day. Another time we had a picnic in her honour a bit beyond Bray Lock, and watched the steam launch of Sir Dhunjibhoy Bomanji glide by with all its polished brass and blinding white paint. Sir Dhunjibhoy was glorious in grey morning-coat with silken lapels and immaculately white jhodpurs. His guests, both white and brown, conversed in an inimitably degagé manner with ladies of varying degrees of beauty and avoirdupois, draped in vividly hued saris. It was a dazzling spectacle, accompanied by the soft swish-swish of the vessel's bow-wave, the animated murmur of distance-modifed conversation and the dulcet sibilants of the steam-valve, rather like a melodious samovar. My pleasure at such a concentrated vision of my beloved idle rich fell like a shot bird in sight of Grandma's outraged visage.

'A BLACKAMORE!' she broke forth, showering us all in her indignation, with a benison of biscuit-crumbs. 'A BLACKAMORE in the seat of the mighty! I've seen everything there is to see now! Ah, this wicked, wicked South!'

I gave Pa a look. The mistiness of his eyes from the wine he had been drinking was suddenly pierced by the knife-edge of his hatred. For a moment he looked truly dangerous — the samurai look.

I was fifteen when Grandma's special penchant revealed itself. I was detailed to escort her to see *The Thief Of Baghdad*, with Douglas Fairbanks senior. It was Saturday. Our way led past the flea-pit in Queens Street (later to be transmogrified into the Plaza in the new Art-Deco age), and there we came to a sudden stop before the lurid stick-up at the entrance.

'This look more inviting than a silly old heathen thief,' she declared with resolution . I gazed at her in shocked amazement.

Extensive Showrooms displaying

ANTIQUE FURNITURE
PORCELAIN
ANTIQUE SILVER
OLD SHEFFIELD PLATE
FINE LEATHER GOODS
DIAMOND JEWELLERY
SOLID SILVER PLATE
SILVER-PLATED WARE
WATCHES & CLOCKS
FANCY JEWELLERY
ETC.

E. T. BIGGS & SONS
30 & 32 HIGH STREET, MAIDENHEAD
TEL. 223

With a burst of dramatic narrative, I demolished Butler's stores, Biggs, the celebrated jeweller . . . 'All that wicked wealth flaunted in the faces of the poor and needy . . .'

'But it , it's about vice!' I told her. '*Flames of Passion.* You can see by the bill. It's about all sorts of vile wickedness. Besides, there are fleas there and sometimes mice come up from the cheap seats!'

'Every good old Norfolk barn have its mice,' she retorted. 'Rats a-plenty too. As for fleas — well, they let me aloone as a rule. Come you on. It'll be a moral lesson for us booth!'

So in we went, after obtaining our tokens from Mr Wright, the Manager, with his wonky Will Hay pince-nez and his terrible temper. These tokens were thin metal plates, pierced at the centre to enable them to be threaded upon a perpendicular metal rod. These were handed to the attendant, who handed them back to Mr Wright, when a certain number had been assembled on a string. I never saw this in any other cinema.

Grandma seemed entirely unaffected by the appalling fugginess of the atmosphere. That of the lowest four-ale bar would have tasted salubrious by comparison. Tobacco-smoke, mouldiness, a ratty redolence and, there was no denying it, a strong scent of urine commingled with gas and orange-peel. At intervals, the strident shriek of a band-saw from the adjoining timber-yard half drowned the tinkling piano, while at each and every high point of the drama the massed urchins down in the 'threepenny's' raised a lusty cheering and whistling, bringing Mr Wright bounding and foaming from his little box, bawling threats of mass ejection. He started these menaces at the very back of the auditorium, thus seeming to apply them to gentle and simple alike. That afternoon there happened a higher number of breakdowns than usual in the operating-box, accompanied by mocking cheers and ribald demands by the urchinry for the return of its money.

Was Grandma perturbed by these disorders? Not one wit. Totally enthralled, she followed the unfolding of that banal melodrama with agonized intentness. It was, of course, all about a beautiful and generously-built woman, persecuted by a drunken, womanizing husband who, and this had long ceased to thrill me, took destructive liberties with her attire. The plot was concerned with her divorce case, involving lurid flashbacks, suborned witnesses (including an appalling black-eyed vamp), and concluded by that false creature stabbing the husband to death, thus leaving the heroine free to marry the elderly but distinguished looking Judge who had tried her case. All the way through Grandma sucked sherbet cushions emotionally, as her sucking breeched the sugar shell, releasing a charge of sherbet, a tiny effervescense reminiscent of a dose of Eno's fruit-salts.

Wafted on foul airs, we emerged blinking into the mellow September sunlight. Grandma had a look of unmistakable catharsis. The entertainment might have been sad rubbish, but Grandma's soul seemed nicely purged.

From the other side of Queens Street, floral and fruity aromas from the shop of the glamorous Mrs Sue Hunt met the Cinema's halitosis headlong, and triumphed by the aid of a lovely odour of fresh-sawn pine planks from the timber-yard. And behold, there stood Muriel, receiving a punnet of fresh figs from the hands of Mrs Hunt, whom the Great War had widowed and who still wept for her lost husband, much to the chagrin of a score of willing bachelors of assorted ages.

I whisked Grandma away with the skill and velocity of a conjuror. She was not, in my opinion, the sort of relative one flashes around. Muriel at fifteen, I had observed with a fluttering heart-beat, dressed in a light summer frock of flowered voile, remained chubby but, possessed of the loveliest pair of legs in creation. Steering Grandma like a human bath-chair up Grenfell Road, I began to fall in love with my first sweetheart all over again. It wouldn't do to waste a lot of time either. Legs the like of hers were as rare as snowballs in Timbuctoo, and her face, despite its puppy-fat....Well, try and imagine the purest peach-skinned Scottish blonde possessed of eyes, sea blue but almond-shaped...slanted like those of a French Indo-Chinese girl!

'He wasn't really a bad looking sort of man,' uttered Grandma suddenly.

'Sorry, Grandma, what — '

'That old man she married in the end. He looked right nice

and hoomely tying up the roses round the door at the end.'

'Right Grandma,' I said and began to yearn for Monday when I would, I decided, fake a bilious attack and catch Muriel before she caught her train for Cygnet Green.

Beneath our feet a County Tanker puffed, with a clanking of couplings, under the Grenfell Road bridge on its way to High Wycombe, its steam billowing up each side of the parapets, enveloping us.

'Dirty old beggar!' ejaculated Grandma in disgust. But I savoured the sulphurous cloud with sensuous delight. The heavy clatter of couplings, the acrid belchings of funnels, like the view across the trees of the County Boys School and the beeches with the scent of their mast in the autumn in Grenfell Park had become during the past two years or so, as much part of the imaginative background of my life as the Thicket, the River and the meadows and fields around Pinkney's Green, Burchets Green, Knowle Hill and Bray. Before I knew it, their influence was to grow more powerful than all the other attractions put together. My first love affair would transform them from banality to sorcery, from everyday ordinariness into a realm of joy and suffering.

'Come on Grandma,' I said. 'Best foot forward.'

'It's all very well for you,' expostulated the old lady.'You haven't got a boon in your leg like me!'

For Grandma was not one to betray a confidence. Thus every effort we made, my brothers and I, to elicit from her the purpose of our parents absence was in vain.

'A still tongue maketh a wise head — Umph!' Or, 'Beware the unruly tongue...!' We gave it up at last, hoping we were worrying about nothing.

No matter how odd her appearance, Mrs Grintforth turned out a jewel of a landlady. She was both plump and broad. Whichever way you looked at her, in profile, full-frontal or from above, she presented a perfect Euclidean square, endowed with feet, hands and a head. Her eyes were narrow and seamed and her long mouth was knife-thin, presenting that geometrical indelicacy, a pointed ellipse. She and

Grandma were a bit starchy with each other at the outset, addressing one another as 'Ma'am', with a slight shiver of dignity; Mrs Grintforth came out best in the end, because of the indomitable massiveness of her square features, the strangely Aztec look with which she surveyed Grandma. She looked to be quite capable, with her primitively chiselled features, of producing a sacrificial knife of obsidian and shedding Grandma's blood as a libation to Quetsalcoatl.

On that Monday afternoon the old girl took Tony off to see Dolores del Rio in *Retribution at the Grand*. After a lunch of tasty lamb mince, french beans and creamed potatoes, followed by bread and butter pudding full of fat sultanas, I got out my writing pad and, drawing out a chair, prepared to get busy with Mooghie's letter.

I had barely made a start when, after a discreet knock, our landlady came in to invite me to her kitchen.

There, despite anxiety as to my parents' doings in Norwich and poignant longing for Mooghie, I spent one of the happiest afternoons of my life. The kitchen was sparkling clean, the range fire glowed ruddily behind its bars, a grey, old-fashioned table-cover invited the meditative elbow to prop itself, whilst from the chimney-piece fascinating, fair-groundy ornaments drew the eye. I particularly admired a little flower-seller in a yellow smock sprigged by tiny bunches of blossoms unknown to any living naturalist. Mrs Grintforth promptly gave it to me.

'That's alright,' she said when I demurred. 'I've got more of 'em than I can rightly do with. All that dust'n — I-I say all that dust'n!' Her habit of repeating final clauses was in no way indicative of a presupposition that you were deaf. It was no more than a nervous habit of speech. We found it delightfully and endearingly funny, I accepted her gift with gratitude.

By four o'clock my letter was finished, a gem of a letter if I do say so. I was obliged to invent an account of my efforts, quite abortive, to establish a psychic rapport with my love. Ten o'clock vigils had failed to conjure up anything beyond floating sparklers on the retina. I was even — and this was more than unnerving — unable to summon up Mooghie's lovely face to my inward eye. I carried in my breast-pocket her tiny handkerchief, sweet with the ghost of her Italian jasmines; I smoked sparingly her gift of Abdullahs; I tenderly cherished in one of Mrs Grintforth's tiny pots the green-gold pinnate leaf of the Lumie Tree. All these mnemonic goodies and I couldn't even call up her exquisite face.

At ten past four, Mrs Grintforth drew new scones from the range and made tea. Something struck the scullery tiles with a crash and a splintering.

'Oh, SHIT!' ejaculated Mrs Grinforth. 'I-I say SHIT!'

In the midst of our mirthful chorus I understood what she had meant about her ornaments.

At five Grandma and Tony returned: the former looking enjoyably harrowed, the latter glum. When Victor arrived soon after wearing the grey flannel slacks I had bought him that morning, there came a sudden belabouring of the front door knocker.

'That's the telegraph lad,' said our landlady, 'I say that's the telegraph lad.' And so it was. Ma and Pa would be away for another four days. Mrs Grintforth's scone came up into my throat as wind. Then, as suddenly, I was my own man again. In that instant, against the creepered garden wall outside, I saw my Mooghie as plain as print...slanting, adorable eyes, delicate nose, honey-blonde hair in sweet disorder, firm, shapely legs and all. She seemed to say to me: 'remember our plans. Don't worry, my darling. Everything will be perfect!'

'What you staring at out of that oold window?' grated Grandma.

'A ghost,' I retorted.

'I wonder,' she rabbitted on 'what keeps them two in Norwich.'

'I couldn't really care less,' I said, noting with glee her falling chops at my new nonchalance. With immense satisfaction I saw dear Mrs Grintforth carry their tray into the chilly dining-room. As she went by she gave me a merry, geometrical, conspiratorial wink.

8

Thundering Canon

Brunel's navvies, in throwing up the railway embankment across the south side of the town, had cut it off from the countryside towards Windsor. Thus, when the morning arrived for me to make my first appearance at the County Boys School, it was with a lively sense of broadening horizons, of adventure and release, that I passed under the railway arch from the urban dinginess of Kings Street into the positively rural quietness and brightness of Shoppenhangers Road, my new-school nerves momentarily forgotten.

Everywhere were mists and mellow fruitfulness. The sun was lifting curtains of vapour from Such's orchards, disclosing fruit-laden pear and apple trees, all dripping and delectable. There must have been a mild, early frost. You could smell it in the air: one of the most evocative smells in nature.

My spirits rose higher. I ran into friends from Queen Anne's new boys like myself, not yet quite accustomed to their school caps and satchels. There was Peter Lloyd, the vet's son and Billy Bird, whose mum kept a cosy little sweet-shop in Bridge Street, as well as Eddie Lakeman, youngest son of the painter, who had a picture-framing establishment and sold artists materials in King Street. And there was Timberlake, the demon Timberlake, of whom more hereafter, with his dancing eyes, fine fresh colouring and every tooth in his head on show whether he laughed or whether he wept.

Chatting self-consciously, we followed Such's spiked railings on the one side and the more formidable ones guarding the railway embankment upon the other. Huge pigs were rooting about for wind-falls around the trees. Their rich smell hung upon the air. Shoppenhangers Road curved up steeply to the left past the golf-links footpath, where foxy-faced caddies lounged, then skirted a fine wood of beeches and oaks; perhaps descendants of those hanging woods from which the Manor of Shoppenhanger originally took its name.

At the brow of the hill on the right stood the School gates, facing the main entrance to the golf-links. I had taken my entrance exam two weeks previously. Then quiet had reigned but for a blustering wind which had covered the road with untimely wrenched acorns. Today the place was strident with boys and bicycles of every sort and condition. Two even had motor-scooters guided by antler-like handlebars.

My companions and I went in together. Timberlake joined us, despite not being one of the Queen Anne set.

'Forsake all hope, all ye that enter here!' he intoned gruesomely, and I for one felt a yearning at the guts.

It was, to use the simple speech of a ten-year old, quite a decent sort of a place. The building was rectangular, of new red brick, with two floors and close-set windows with white-painted frames. The Headmaster's house, handsome and in a similar style, stood to the right of the main gate, partly concealed by a rich rash of rambler roses, out of which, with surrealistic unexpectedness, the mouth of a giant howitzer gaped heavenward. To the right of the School's front door rested a cross between a sausage and an enormous toy aeroplane, a paravane. Separated by deep gravel, the two buildings might understandably have been mistaken for a small military academy, which in a certain ridiculous sense, they were. On the South side, enclosed by laurels, stretched two well-kept tennis-courts. These, in their immaculate greenness appeared to be for private use. At the south front an asphalt playground separated the main backdoors from the bogs and bicycle-sheds, while around the corner, approached by an extremely rough and dangerous tract of flints, lay the Headmaster's pride and joy: the senior gamesfield, provided for the winter-term with goal-posts. A sloping bank of grass, lined with young birches and a split-chestnut fence, separated the Quad, as it was rather pretentiously known (it was, in fact, roughly triangular) from the holy ground. Originally a grey fence had bounded the demesne, but then Lord Desborough had presented an extensive area beyond the School fence, which waste-land 'volunteers' from among the less academically enthusiastic were slowly transforming into new playing-fields and a Parade Ground!

A PARADE-GROUND! After the inspissated mud and blood and wireslung human rot of the late 'Great' War, with a good half of one's mother's friends widowed and hopelessly disconsolate, in a world where they outnumbered what men remained by the million, like poor, lovely Sue Hunt and Mrs Bird and pretty Mrs Spratly, the Corsetiere in King Street; with stumps and crutches and smashed and burnt faces everywhere, wouldn't it have been reasonable to expect that the collective back might have turned resolutely and forever and a day upon war and all its works? Not at County Boys School.

The County Boys' School — with the Headmaster's pride and joy: the gamesfield, parade ground and the Cadet Corps.

A cadet-corps flourished. The rest of us were, for the space of Friday afternoon, known as the Company B. We were the Pariah Squad, but were obliged to march up and down and to and fro, right-forming with comic confusion, left-forming in a sudden calamitous flurry of collapsing limbs. Bugles blew in vain to inspire us with military fervour. Junior Masters who had survived the holocaust were obliged to resume, for a few hours, the Kings uniform and to drill unwilling, half-defiant, wholly derisive boys of every age. The uniformed cadets, the élite, bore heavy carbines from the Boer War, while the despised remainder shouldered mocked up muskets, consisting of crudely carved stocks (products of forced labour during wood-work classes), lengths of narrow iron piping, and dummy bolts and triggers. Fire-arms weapons lined two walls of the handicraft shed; the former two racks in the Prefects' Common Room, their oily stench mingling with that of stale crumbs from the prefects' sandwiches and their post-prandial wind.

The Head's chief ambition in life seemed to be the winning of something called the 'Lucas Tooth' for victory in an annual inter-schools military tournament. This mystery turned out to be a simple cup of silver, but I had a satyrical vision of an immense molar, drawn posthumously from the jaws of an heroic Brass Hat called Lucas, and thereafter mounted in a rich golden setting. I never saw the thing, because we never won it.

That first morning after prayers, followed by a somewhat muddling allocation of text-books, forms and form-masters, I found myself trotting down to the playing fields with 3B for Drill. Not gym, not jerks, but DRILL.

In fours we marched and counter-marched. In fours we settled down at last to the usual, time-honoured Swedish exercises, and here I earnt my first and almost sole commendation of that term.

'Hips firm! Feet together! Trunk forward bend!' cried Joey Legget, my new form-master. He was a handsome chap with a small soft moustache, a spotless handkerchief tucked into his sleeve and, in his well-cut suit of indigo serge, the absolute epitome of a period type known as The Knut. He only needed the bowler hat, cane and eye-glass to resemble almost exactly the trade-mark of the Sharps Kreemy Toffee Company. I

H. REEVES

Wholesale and Retail
CONFECTIONER. . .

75 *Queen Street, MAIDENHEAD*

*The Popular Shop for Chocolates,
Toffees, and Sweets by all best makers*
Fancy and Weight Boxes a Speciality

The Noted Shop for CREAM ICES during Season

*Queen Street — the home of Reeves' sweetshop and, in
particular, retailer of Sharps Kreemy Toffee.*

obeyed his commands with alert eagerness, albeit with thoughts characteristically astray.

'Good position, Woolf!'

I held my breath and my good position. I had DONE WELL!

At that moment there came from the main building the sound of boys singing. Their voices, high, sweet and melodious, rang distantly in the mellow September air. What song they sang I have never, strangely enough, learnt to this day, though I heard it often. Perhaps I didn't want to know its title, for fear it might disillusion me about the romantic dreams its strains conjured up in my mind. It suggested to me the simple sadness of a milk-maid bearing the heavy yoke upon her strong, shapely shoulders and longing for her lad, fighting in the wars far away — perhaps already fallen.

Before the ending of that song, their voices were checked, and I cursed the petty fogging old domini responsible for cutting off such a delightful source of pleasure. But it soon took up again.

At that moment we were allowed a rest. Joey Legget fell into conversation with one or two of the chaps, and I found a nice little mushroom on the bank, green-latticed by the grasses it had pushed its way through. This I peeled and nibbled as I listened to the milk-maid's lament. An engine was shunting its line of trucks on the line beyond Railway Wood, sparrows cheeped and fluttered on the roof of the woodwork shed, Bill Thatcher, grey-wavey and grizzled, goundsman and care-taker, began to rake at the turf nearby, sending a wafture of thyme to our nostrils.

Muriel's image sprang to my mind with a totally unexpected impact. Her warm-blonde hair, her sea-blue eyes, her soft yet resilient movements, her dear chic little drawers . . . She was the milk-maid of whom they were, or ought to be, singing with their flawless young voices. It became number one in a series of Muriel-songs that my mind, almost unconsciously, began to collect, until one never-to-be-forgotten day, she stopped being my sturdy, chubby little chum and became Mooghie, the living personification of the Thames-side Maidenhead I so loved. The two syllables, with their Oriental overtones, caught vividly the exotic quality of the river's slow summer journey between wide-spreading banks, fields and gardens, sleeping in the sun, weighting the air with rich scents of big, lolling roses, peculiarly foreign-smelling heliotrope and bergamot. On stripey lawns, where slow leaf-shadow danced the Pavane, ladies took tea served by parlourmaids transformed from Hodge's 'gels' into female rarities, only slightly less celestial than their mistresses.

'Wake up, Woolf!'

I shot to my feet, resumed my place in the ranks.

'Pull your stomach in, boy!'

I took a startled look down. Had that mushroom been a toadstool? I was no botanist. Was I already swelling up like a poisoned pup? I breathed again. Joey Legget had addressed an unhealthy-looking specimen called Bates.

The singing had stopped. We marched back to our form-room, which faced the tennis courts. On the way, we encountered 4B. I saw them with a sensation of intense shock. How could such a band of young desperados of such hideous aspect have found those angelic notes, to call up a Greuze milk-maid to my imagination. Definitely a case of the song, not the singer!

Our form-room was painted beige. The shoulders of years of boys had smeared a band of drab grubbiness around the walls. There were two pictures: Napoleon's retreat from Moscow by Meissonier and The Raft Of The Medusa by Genicault. They were in monochrome, and it was not only their subjects that expressed utter lugubriousness. My heart turned over with appalling nostalgia for Queen Anne House.

On a chill, drear Sunday morning soon after Christmas, Renee, Victor, Julie Jacobson from next door and myself elected to call Canon Drummond up from the grave. We were all, it must be said, more than old enough to know better.

The Canon, former incumbent of the Church of All Saints, was a legend in his own lifetime for swinging puritanism. He opposed the first Bioscope, damned the new Hippodrome, cursed the erection of the Skating Rink. Jazz to him was a sickness of the soul. Not a single joy-bringer to human-kind but that he condemned it to the eternal bonfires.

When war raged obscenely over the bloody salient at Ypres, he was there as a Padre and lost a leg. I was too young to remember him, but his physical description was etched indelibly upon my mind by his former parishioners' awed description of his final image: that of a tall, crabbed, irascible, maniacal figure in a flat, round black hat, long black coat and one funereal buttoned gaiter on his surviving leg; swinging himself angrily along on crutches, which seemed to have absorbed a fierce charge of his withering hatred of sin, and to be stabbing about for it in all directions in order to crush it into the sod.

The bell was, if I may so put it, ringing in the Eucharist, and we, having rifled our missionary envelopes for the unholy purchase of sweets from a cheap and cheerful little Sunday-opening shop, kicked our heels in the dank shadow of the Church wall, half-wishing we had attended and, moreover, not a little conscience stricken at having robbed the poor little tinder on India's coral strand of one and fourpence. It would have been warm in Church, even though the Altwood girls were still on vacation. Leaving Victor and me with nobody worth ogling. Satan was by. Eight idle hands were at his disposition, and he put them to work!

The Canon's tomb was simple, but extraordinarily imposing: rich, not gaudy. Above a tall cross, a tiled shelter added to its grandeur. West-facing rested his peg-legged skeleton, all ready, come the day of judgement, to dress down those members of his East-directed flock not doing the right thing. I would have liked to have memorised this scourge of sin's epitaph but, alas, it has gone completely from my mind.

We positioned ourselves at each corner of his wide, high kerb-stone, balancing with some difficulty against the freshening wind, now soughing mournfully through the cedars in the Vicarage garden. Said Julie, out of the blue:

'What say we wake the old beggar up?'

'What? — Like Lazarus?' jerked out Victor in alarm.

Renee looked aghast. In her sturdy nature, mischief ever tended to struggle with a strong regard for the conventions.

'It would be blasphemy,' she said sternly, 'against our Lord's miracles.'

'I don't mean anything to upset our Lord,' argued Julie. 'Just to have his bogey glide up so's we can have a peek at him. Come on, don't be a lot of spoil-sports.'

'I'm game!' Victor did an irreverent little dance on the kerb.

'O.K.' I warned. 'But he won't look too good, you know. Not after all this time. Remember the Monkey's Paw.'

'Never heard of it!' said Julie scornfully. 'Well, what about it, Renee? you're not a cowardy custard usually!'

Worthiness struggled briefly with reluctance to be left out. Renee skipped nimbly back to her corner. 'All right,' she said sourly, 'but it'll be your silly fault if he won't go back in his coffin!'

Julie's huge grin faltered. 'Gracious goodness, I hadn't thought about that.'

'Do we or don't we?' snapped Victor with impatience. 'Make up your silly minds. It's getting bally cold out here.'

'What shall we say?' We looked at each other uncertainly. It was Renee, in whom the desire for leadership took precedence over every other consideration, who provided the necessary formula.

'Let's say "Arise, Canon Drummond, from your dreadful bed of mould, and show thyself unto us — just for a minute!" and make the sign of the Cross — just to make it all Holy!'

So, first throwing shifty looks all around us, we intoned her words in slightly trembling chorus.

'Arise, Canon Drummond, from your dreadful bed of mould, and show thyself unto us — just for a minute!' We waited, crossing ourselves with slow reverence. A blackbird flew down with a scrap of crust in its coral beak, saw us, dropped it in panic and flew up, straight as a rocket, with a nerve-shattering squawk.

'Oh, Jemimah!' screamed Julie, like many instigators, the first to lose her nerve, 'an omen! God forgive us all!'

And then, quite spontaneously, I was seized by diabolical inspiration. Stepping right on to the frost-bitten grass of the grave, avoiding a few bunches of snow-drops in vases and pastepots and a singularly unattractive-'immortelle', I declaimed, one claw upraised, the following atrocious summons:

'Oh, Canon, UNCLAY THYSELF!'

As I uttered that sinister call, a frog sprang to my throat, bringing my voice down an entire octave in a gruff, unearthly rasp that might have been the harsh cry of a gryphon.

I found them staring in horrified dismay at my face, as if I were the risen anti-Christ. Their visages expressed such consternation that my heart began to beat, and with such violence, that beneath my feet the earth of the Canon's grave seemed to lift and fall like the floor of a cake-walk. For one mad moment I felt that I had actually initiated the commencement of the fearful day. I sprang off that grass like a startled lizard. We ran. Breathless and pallid, we joined the emergent congregation, gratefully losing ourselves in its numbers. Renee drew level with me. 'It was the Devil's voice proceeding from your lips!' she accused me. 'I don't see how I can eat my tea with you this afternoon.'

'Then eat it in your own home!' I retorted. 'I just got a frog in my throat, that's all. Nothing to make such a song and dance about!'

'You're a damned soul, that's for sure,' commented Julie.

'Yes,' I replied, 'and so are you after what I saw going on behind our privet hedge last Monday!'

Julie looked startled, flushed and was silent.

'You know,' speculated Victor coolly, 'we may not have brought him up for ourselves, you know. None of us is a ghost-seer, as like as not. We must keep our eyes and ears open, mustn't we?'

And so we did. Then days or so later, Mrs Egbert saw the Canon emerge from the chalky roots of the wayside beeches on

Punt Hill, and stand before her, staring starkly into her eyes. She screamed and stumbled from her bicycle. For a few seconds more he swayed there before, with a screw-like twisting of his flowing black coat, he turned back and crutched himself into the solid earth.

Five minutes later, we heard the clank of her bike against our front fence, the slamming of our front gate, then the door-knocker rattled like a tocsin.

All Saints church Pageant in 1922 posed not 50 paces from Canon Drummond's grave.

In the peacefully hissing gas-light, the scents of tea and toast and the cosy whiff of gently scorching chair-legs (Ma liked her fire piled half way up the chimney), Mrs Egbert's tale fell flat as a pancake. Julie and I were present and even we were unmoved. Julie's mother and mine fed her tea and sympathy, but obviously without giving much credence to her story, because Mrs Egbert had a weakness for uttering tall and ghastly stories, often using them as a pretext for dropping in upon her friends at tea-time. Furthermore, she was an outstanding member of the Maidenhead Amateur Operatic and Dramatic Company. Julie and I believed her in a limited and unemotional way. Besides, there were Spindlers' éclairs for tea, and we were busy. Too busy for Mrs Egbert and the Canon.

The story got around as stories will, and soon we ghost-raisers had our minds relieved.

Every other person in the district took to seeing the Canon. Not to see his shade somewhere or other made a nobody of you. To old Mrs Nettles, he popped up from behind her lavatory door, and Mrs Barfield, the butcher's wife, found him surveying the Avenue from her front bedroom window. There came a night when three people saw him simultaneously, at considerable distances one from another. This reduced haunting to pure absurdity, and Julie and I were able to look Victor and Renee in the eye once more. But the four of us persisted in believing Mrs Egbert; for whether it was from Twyford, White Waltham or Pinkney's Green she returned, she never again came by way of Punt Hill, whether by daylight or candlelight, but always took the long way all around Tittle Row and Boyne Hill.

Curiously, twenty years later on, being at Preston on a tour with ENSA, I was fingering some volumes on a second-hand shelf of a book-shop in a street off Winkley Square. A rather attractive dust-cover caught my eye. I picked it up, then dropped it rather quickly. It was by Theodore Powys. Its title was *Unclay*. It gave me quite a turn.

9

Fires and Brimstone

From thoughts of Canon Drummond it is a short, mental step to a vision of roaring, leaping flames.

On a dark, dry, winter's night with grit on the fierce north-westerly wind, Gordon Road Laundry caught fire, and burned to the ground in a noble holocaust.

Returning from the Windsor Castle, my father had his attention caught by a sprite-like glimmer of wandering luminosity, dancing from window to window of the Laundry at the top of Gordon Road. Shaken in a trice from his euphoria, he took to his heels, paused at our back gate and decided that a really first-rate fire, if it should so turn out, might prove both pleasureable and instructive to his son and heir, now two years old and an odd bit.

Thus, five minutes later, I reclined in his lean, muscular arms, and warmly wrapped up in a shawl and a rug, rapturously observing the budding, burgeoning and finally the bursting forth of a great flower of towering flames, that gobbles up joists, rafters, lathe and plaster after silhouetting them with dreadful brevity against the mottled sky, then spitting them out in glowing gobbets and driftings; snipping off enormous sheets of flame so that, for a tiny space of time, they lifted and fluttered in splendid isolation before vanishing into nothingness. Red hot slates splintered and cracked like dragons' scales. The main chimney came thundering down, and a magnificent banner of sparks shot sky-ward...a superfine roman-candle. The spectators fell back in alarm, expecting Pa, who gave way only when, rather belatedly, the fire engine sped, rattling and clanging furiously, up Wellington Road: a one-storey, old fashioned thing, with shallowly slanted ladder, enormous radiator and broad, solid tyres. It was high time too, for that bleak north-wester had joined forces with the whirl-wind flames engender of themselves, and neighbouring roofs lay beneath menacing fiery fingers.

I am persuaded that on reflection, that Gargantuan conflagration was the intensest, purest pleasure of my life. Too young and egocentric to pity, or identify myself with, the laundresses and other personnel, who watched in agony their jobs going up with their previous day's tasks: shirts, skirts, sheets, long-johns, blankets and bloomers; ledgers, benches and waggons — the horses had early been saved and led into an apple-orchard lower down the hill — I drank in avidly, greedily, every slightest sensation of pleasure from that grand, streaming, pulsating blaze. For me nothing marred it. It was splendidly perfect and when, quite suddenly, the roof fell in, then the walls; when a great gush of heat drew a stifled breath of panic from the crowd, and even our windows right down on the corner of the Avenue blazed into temporary glory. I experienced a delicious sense that we had our own particular slice of the general glory of the grand disaster.

At last hoses and axes triumphed over chaos. The glow faded from the sky. Only a few sprinklings of sparks remained; only an occasional hollow sound of falling plank on plank. Reluctantly the neighbours turned homeward. The local constable mounted his bicycle and disappeared into the now darkened road. As for me . . . I was sound off before Pa reached the first of our lilac-trees.

Now if there was one thing in particular that fiery fiesta did for me, beside give me unalloyed pleasure, it was this: for whereas those outside my immediate circle had had no separate existence for me, but had moved like orbital shadows around me, now those flaming brands and, above all, that ultimate, all-revealing collapse of the entire structure had shown them to me as individual entities. From then on I learned names and faces, identified personalities and individualities, grew curious — sometimes too curious about their lives and their affairs. Mrs Cartware and her son, a bookmakers' clerk, imprisoned for doing something devious wtih his employer's telephone and the racing results; old Mrs Hole and her simpleton grandson,

*Long after the Gordon road Laundry fire, in the late '20s,
J.A. Boura & Co offered their rather sad swansong service to
Maidonians.*

103

whose parents had abandoned him for lives of pleasure; massive old Mrs Brown who 'drank'; and Mary-Anne Collier in Powney Road, whose expulsion from Boyne Hill Church School had been a breathless scandal.

Not all at once came understanding of their personalities and predicaments, of course. But I had made a start on the way to discovering the dodges of the world and its wayfarers. By the time I was eight or nine and imbued with a stronger sense of intuition, Tommy Cartware had done two more stretches in Reading Gaol, Mrs Brown was soggy as a rotten melon with the dropsy, and Mary-Anne Collier had two more rather brutish-looking waifs by the rude and licentious soldiery.

But it was the great Laundry Fire that had me, newly gregarious, trotting about, a human come out from the fog of babyhood.

Fire, if it had afforded me bounding, uninhibited joy at the Gordon Road Inferno, inspired me with nothing but perturbation, even terror, on the night, soggily damp but rainless, of The Torchlight Procession: culmination of the Armistice night fire-works and general celebrations on the Moor.

This Procession was a popular — even proletarian — jollification. Many respectable folk feared the worst . . . particularly those whose dwellings were in the streets to be taken by the revellers. It was exactly the sort of thing that might very well get thoroughly out of hand, and end in a thousand torches put to a thousand homes in a dire explosion of class-hatred, rapine, slaughter and an irreparable crashing down of every barrier raised by Society against itself!

What made it worse for use was the absence of Pa — still in Archangel and, it seemed, likely to be there indefinitely. No Armistice for him, poor man.

Ma was less than useless to us as a shield against danger and destruction. Missing and worrying about Pa had reduced her to a hollow-eyed ghost, with gaunt, ageing cheeks. Nightly she barricaded us all in one room behind extra bolts, with a chair-back jammed beneath the door-knob.

In the dank darkness lit only by our street-corner light, by our front gates we waited, half fearful, half stimulated, glad of the company of our neighbours from Gordon and Wellington Roads. Talk was quiet and quite soothing, save for the occasional saw-edged laughter of old Mrs Nettles, and the staccato cackle of Mr Dean. And all at once there wobbled past the dim oil lamp of Constable Sterry's old bone-shaker.

'They're coming!' he called out. 'It's all Sir Garnet. They're peaceful as lambs. Stand by your gates and give 'em a rousing cheer!'

It was from Belmont Road they came. Headed by the Maidenhead Silver Band, they swept into the Avenue like a stream of molten lava, their torches transforming the autumn leaves from ripe golden to bloody scarlet. Torches waved in all directions set up a pattern of chaotic geometry, strangely and weirdly ordered by the rhythm of their marching feet. The band silenced itself. Alone the big drum throbbed breast-shakingly. Suddenly it was Colonel Bogey. The throng, as if freshly liberated by the martial, impudent strains, brandished their torches, and gave out with the full unexpurgated version of Britain's War-Song. Some, notably a knot of slatternly women, raggle-taggle Boadiceas, struck up the cry of 'Hang The Kaiser!' which spread back to those following behind. Abruptly the band drew level with our gate, then the main body. The horribly unkempt clothing of both sexes was enough to put you off applause. However, we did manage a hoarse, weazen shout. I felt sick at the sight of those black, shapeless, ankle-length skirts, those battered boots and shoes resembling marching cudgels, and black, wrinkled suits and flat cloth caps. Most of them wore the 'choker' and the tin 'albert' strung across the threadbare waistcoat. From every slum in many-slummed Maidenhead they came . . . A credit to every Victorian-descended Alderman. From Moffat Street, from the Barracks, from East Street, they came . . . From Brocks Lane and Ray Street and North-end Council Estate and Chummies Row. Most of them I never seemed to have seen before that night. Others, slinking boys and girls, I had seen too often for comfort. They had kicked blood from our shins and abused us. Now they sped by with their hobnails striking sparks from the road, whirling winter-warmers made from tins slung on strings containing rags and other combustible materials. They swept past shouting, but there was little joy about them. At the height of the ghastly illumination, with those stinking torches causing the gaudy chestnut leaves to shiver on their weakening stalks, the general facial expression was a sour resolution to be noticed, to be accepted as fellow human beings by the rest of us. And, in the middle of it all, up sprang Joey, the Town clown: a terrible creature, painted, primped, tri-wigged like Whimsical Walker; with slashed velvet shoes and a shockingly CLEAN ruffled collar. Against the frenziedly moving backdrop of flaring torch-light, tatterdemalion capering, red and sweaty faces, that collar was an offence to the senses; a nightmare incongruity.

He jigged about before us, stinking with sweat, gibbering behind his paint in a shrill, ramish voice of brutish indecency. Trembling, I took the coppers Ma held out to me. All at once it struck me that I'd felt out of sorts all day; that what had been ailing me was about to catch up.

'HANG THE KAISER!' howled the never-ending mob, deafening, yet simultaneously very far away. At that very moment, Joey's grimacing wound of a face stretched itself like inexhaustible elastic above the gate; a red plush bag was thrust into my face, a sickening greasy thing I was sure I couldn't under any consideration bring myself to touch. That repulsive Punchinello-cackling struck sudden ice to my very heart. Desperately I endeavoured to chuck the pennies into that scarlet, throat-like cavity. My arm became a lead weight. The coins fell anywhere. I dropped in a heap on the damp lawn.

I came to myself in delectable tranquillity, sitting upon somebody's mackintosh, supported in the arms of Miss Gough, one of the Gordon Road school-teachers. It was she who had ordered everyone but Mrs Jacobson out of the garden.

I was scared at first. Isn't anybody, coming out of a faint? I soon recovered when Mrs Jacobson practically blew off the top of my head with her smelling-bottle. Miss Gough helped me to

The Great Torchlight Procession was the culmination of Armistice Night and they marched down the Avenue like molten lava. Mr George Baker fed 2,500 of much the same crowd, a year later, on Recognition Day 1919.

my feet and, aided by her and Mrs Jacobson, I was feebly placing one foot before the other, when something very odd and eerie came to pass. Ma, hitherto in a quasi—cataleptic state, lifted her finger and murmered, 'Listen.'

We all came to a halt on the front path in the dim, divinely restored lamplight. The stench of those cursed torches still lay heavily on the chilly humid air. The Avenue was deserted.

And without any further warning there came to our ears a furtive fluttering and pattering of falling leaves. In a steady, perpendicular shower they descended, brushing our faces like phantom fingers, rattling their strong stalks upon the window-panes, carpeting the Avenue and its gardens in scarlet and gold. Everywhere now was laden with the strange seminal scent of dying chestnut leaves.

'Those filthy torches,' complained Miss Gough acidly. 'Robbing us of our autumn!'

Ma, recovering now that the threat of bloody revolution was past, bent and looked into my face.

'His colour's coming back,' she remarked, and then, as if the idea might substantially bring comfort to me:

'We thought we had lost you, my darling. Your little heart almost stopped beating.'

Quietly in my ear I heard Miss Gough's disgusted comment:

'Bloody, dammed fool of a woman! Your heart's as right as rain. Lots of little boys have a fainting spell now and again!'

That very night I resolutely refused to enter a nightly cage and Ma, I have to hand it to her, refused with equal resolution to lock me out. It did us both the world of good. I entered with joy and relief my nice, airy little bedroom — until Grandma's next visit, when Ma moved back to the matrimonial couch and I turned in with Victor. But by then it was late spring, and the marvellous Begonia Grandiflora was already flourishing the red-brown fists of its buds, and thrusting its juicy pinnate leaves in at the open window. The sparrows' fledglings, perched on its magnificent double stem, fretfully shook their wings for food. It was a good spring and, though we knew it not, Pa was on his way home. He turned up one morning, thin as a rail, his chest twice the size, with presents all round.

He looked at grandma, grinned shortly and turfed her out! She shogged off to her elder daughter at Harrow, muttering curses on all soldiers untimely returned to their homes and families.

Between the Workhouse and Newells' Bakery, at the junction of the Avenue and St Mark's Road, a tall, spiked iron fence enclosed the Workhouse field. Fifty yards or so within a locked gate, a former gravel-pit, small when compared to others in the Road, had become a rubbish-tip. The one-horse tumbrils of the local contractor, Peter Brill, dumped Corporation rubbish there, to which many surrounding house-holders managed, as demonstrated by suspicious-looking holes in neighbouring hedges, to add subsidiary contributions of that minor domestic detritus which looks and smells like nothing else on this earth. Rusty iron bed-heads, rotten totty-pots, hideous scraps of linoleum, old clothes, and more readily perishable trash best left unmentioned, filled up the chasm year after year, and all this ironically convenient, to the Fever Hospital in one direction, and the Private Cemetery in the other.

On a hot summer Sunday afternoon, following a long period of rainlessness, the entire stinking mass took fire. A broken bottle-end, perhaps, acted as a burning glass, or a spark from some back-garden weed-fire . . . Whatever it was, flames were soon leaping furiously from that festering accumulation, grasses and weeds crackling viciously and blinding, evil-smelling smoke made the sweltering sunlight lurid and ghastly.

We saw the flames, almost invisible though they were in the sun's glare, heard their bellow and crepitation all the way from Spindlers' garden, and in two minutes we stood clasping the railings, with the Jacobson brood and hosts of the local urchinry, cheering the ardent but harmlessly bounding and cavorting flames. Harmless, because the barley crop had been cut and carried early.

Old Mr Banwell, my music teacher's father, had hurried across from Pennystone Road, abandoning his tea, and now stood beside me, singing Verdi's *Strida La Vampa* with apposite gusto, cultured old gentleman.

Exhibiting its customary tardiness, came the fire-engine. The gates were thrown open, down leapt the firemen, the hoses were unwound, the pumps began to pant. Alas, the hydrant turned out to be as dry as an aged cow, and it looked as if the inferno would have its way. But wet sacks were fetched from nearby houses, and aged paupers could be seen bearing buckets of water from the Union. True they spilt most of it on the way across but they meant well, poor old dears! In the smoke-shadowed glow the brass helmets shone dully. Mr Banwell began to warble *The Burning Of Troy*. It was very soon obvious that wet sacks and homoepathic doses of water would do little to douse the inferno. The fire captain ordered everybody back.

All at once, as if in obedience to a signal, the rats began to leave the stinking ship. With their uncanny humpity trot, their pelts ablaze, they emerged from the holocaust. Many of them, their ventral gasses expanding, blew themselves up like bombs. Pop! they went: Pop-Poppity-Pop! all over the place, with here and there a violent little puff of vapour! It was intensely exciting.

At last the pyre began slowly to subside. Smoke thickened, eyes smarted and ran. The firemen wound up the abortive hose, and soon the engine drove away, leaving behind a pair of personnel in case of a fresh outbreak, and to chase off the kids from Portlock and Powney Road, who were showing a tendency to invade the scene armed with sticks, in hot pursuit of the surviving rats who, dazed by the noisome fumes, ran fitfully to and fro, squealing pitifully.

Suddenly a cheer arose. In the middle distance, a pair of weird figures emerged from the smoke, kicking up sparks from a still smouldering patch, coughing and whooping wildly, their boots and trousers well afire. They revealed themselves at last as Wally Bidwell, our manure, gathering friend, and Monkey-Man, who was nobody's friend, another our local grotesques, with his chimp's upper-lip and his evil eye, the complete antithesis of the friendly Wally and, I had felt ever since I reached my early teens, a genuine menace. Alas, how dangerous he really was I was to discover one day to my bitter and nearly tragic cost. But at the moment their dancing drollery had us all in stitches of laughter. They made me think of a couple of phoenixes rising in crazy triumph from their own ashes. But, with no ceremony at all, the two firemen drove them off, after beating out the sparks from their scintillating legs. Conscious at last of their injuries, they howled like banshees as they stumbled through the hedge.

Soon — by 1931 — the awful brick caskets extended almost to Pinkneys Green . . . the burning of the punts and the horrid coming of the cabin cruiser: not quite the same view from the bridge as here, nearly twenty years before.

'E finita la musica, e passata la carnevale!' quoth Mr Banwell, and turned back to Pennystone Road and his tea, leaving us in trouble. We had missed Sunday School and Sunday School for us was a special one for we 'naice' little boys and girls at the Vicarage where, under the protection of a slightly bearded lady called Miss Bowler, we were supposed to be safe from the stripes and blows of the bigger Boyn Hill toughs who attended the main Church School. Though a tiny bit guilty, we felt it had been well worthwhile to have played hookey. The drifting fiery flakes; the immense heat which had seemed to threaten the very eyeballs with glutinous

111

dissolution; the funny antics of the frustrated firemen; and, at the end, that grotesque dance of the two phoenixes and all those exploding rats . . . Pop! Poppity-Pop!

Mingling with the dispersing crowd. I ran into Betty Venables, the prettiest girl in the Avenue, with her fair, thick wavy hair and delicious corraline mouth. If she had seen fit to cut Sunday-School then there could be little harm in it.

'Let's go for a little walk,' she invited.

'Where to?' I inquired.

'What about the Lovely Fields and back by the Thicket?'

'Alright,' I took a quick squint at her lips. Their prettiness was a little limp, and quivering over her white teeth. With a sure instinct, I was aware that for the moment she had laid aside her virtue — at least a very little of it — and that I might very well expect to be kissed amid the still-unharvested wheat and the arterially scarlet poppies of those same 'Lovely Fields.' We set off. I had an idea her heart, bless it, was beating as fast as my own.

When, somewhat later, I first clapped my eyes on a print of Monet's Poppy-Field, it was to those fields of ours at Maidenhead, on the way to Pinkney's Green, that my memory immediately returned. Alas, five years later, the place was covered with jerry-built houses, and the fine tall elms at its northern end were down, the huge, rusty iron post where sweethearts met through all our childhood and youth uprooted. Soon — by 1931 — the awful brick caskets extended almost to Pinkney's Green, but by that time I was no longer around to see and suffer it, or the burning of the punts and skiffs, and the horrid coming of the cabin cruiser.

10

That's Entertainment

Those first two years at the County Boys School were, academically, a dead loss. Pa was a long time forgetting or forgiving the first school report. A vain man, he took it hard that his first-born failed to turn out a genius. Apart from good marks in English and French, the rest of it demonstrated me as an idiot as surely as my exhibition in a freak-show. For weeks after, he went around making me feel a thorough toad. But he perked up when I passed my advanced senior with honours at the Victoria College of Music and bought me a bike: my half-breed Pilot.

Poor scholar I may have been, but I was certainly not lazy. Two and a half hours a day I slaved at the piano on top of my schoolday and so I practically turned my back on homework. What is more I became a great reader. I could not see anything inconsistent in coming home with Balzac's *Old Goriot* in one pocket and *The Magnet* in the other. I had got into the habit of calling at Mr Brown's at the bottom of Castle Hill, for the magazine, and school-boys, in the main, are conservative by nature.

There were three shops at the bottom of Castle Hill: Mr Brown's, a hardware shop, and Woodrough, the butcher. The hardware merchant I never saw; Mr Woodrough was, like his son, short, red and cocky. Dicky was my form-captain and incredibly bossy and self opinionated. His extroverted nature certainly imposed upon mine. If Dicky was Harry Wharton of the Remove, then I was Skinner, the cad from study 7. He made me feel an unenthusiastic slacker. I dodged him as much as possible.

But Mr Brown was something entirely different, and his shop was a perfect Elysium for the younger of his customers.

With the sure instinct of the child-lover he contrived to stock counter, window and shelf with fascinating playthings to be found at no other toyshop in town. Furthermore, his wired boards at the door held every sort of comic, base, common or popular, published at that super-period of the genre. *The Rainbow, Chick's Own, Puck, Lot'O Fun, Kinema Comic, Film Fun, Chips, Comic Cuts* and dozens more. The smell of the printer's ink that came off them intoxicated you with anticipatory joy. To use the words of the book reviewers of the time: it was 'sheer delight.' Mr Brown was also a tobacconist and, as with a newsagent, opened early in the morning. So that he was besieged by business men of every kind for cigarettes and tobacco. He sold everything in that line from Saint Julien to shag. It was in Brown's that I first set eyes on Peter Timberlake, another devotee of Frank Richards, though his chosen novelist was Alexandre Dumas.

Mr Brown was one of the neatest men I ever saw, with his dark suit, spotless white shirts and collars and sober neckwear. Like Joey Legget, he carried his handkerchief in his left cuff. I recall the wonderful Christmas parties he gave for his childrens' friends; the prodigally expensive gifts and the magnificent Christmas tree, the blazing fire up the chimney and the dazzling delights of the tea table.

His children, Reggie, Doris and Desmond, he rather surprisingly elected to send to Gordon Road School, where they picked up the local lingo, which might have been alright for the boys, but was positively linguistic disaster for poor Doris. She was so very pretty, with a frenchified look about her, an exquisite little blonde thing who got the habit at an early age of dashing from their front gate in Saint Marks Road, embracing you with violence and crying: 'You're moi li'le swee' ha-art!' Which took all the romance from the huge white bow in her pretty hair.

I got a thing about Kings Street. A born cultist, Kings Street came to find a strong place in my affections, because of its homely down-townness, its frowzy matiness, and because, I must confess it, I have a natural leaning toward the vulgar. The pub smells got me, and the vinegary sweetness of the tatty little fruiterers, where they specialised in garden herbs of every sort. It was a mixture, was Kings Street. Owen Price, the hairdresser, was there on the corner of the Broadway, opposite the corn chandler, Geo. Mattingly, whose daughter was such an accomplished punter. Penn's the bookshop was there, and Penn, the son, was a schoolmate of mine, a perfect stinker of a boy, his soul abounding with meanness and cruelty, who got himself expelled in the end. His father was almost as neat as Mr Brown, but not quite. I think his failure even to compete was due to an inward lack. Mr Brown was a choicer spirit.

But to King Street I will again return. You cannot render in a single paragraph what it takes years to absorb into your soul. Then there's my first caning at the enormous hands of my Headmaster.

It had seemed completely unfair that homework should be expected on top of a day at school, and a long and tiring piano practice. I therefore simply ignored it. I was weary at the day's end, and there was not a soul to whom I might turn, except Mrs Bales, and she showed a surprising reluctance to put in a timely and kindly oar. So what I did was to chuck my satchel in the corner, and apply myself either to good old Frank Richards, or to the *Ghost Stories* of M.R. James. The result was a piling up of complaints, culminating in a summons to the Headmaster's study one rainy afternoon during my fourth week.

I came out with a white face and a scarlet butt. So great had been my dread of that thick, incredibly bendy torture-twig. I only just resisted the temptation to give way to theatrical tears, in an attempt to soften the man's heart. One look at him was enough to dry up my ducts: one of the most handsome chaps I ever saw, six feet tall and broad with it, hair grizzled and wavy with a moustache to match, elegant dark grey suit, spotless linen and a black knitted tie. His brilliant dark blue eye was that of a highlander. I could see him with a claymore in his hand in place of his puissant chastiser. Formalities were short. He held out the list of my misdemeanours; I nodded and said 'Yes, sir.' He placed a small sheet of paper at the middle of his billiards table. The chair was already in place. He said: 'Pick up the paper, Woolf.'

The following three cuts were like sword swipes. For a second or two I lay across the table, breathless and dizzy. Then I heard his voice as if from a cloud.

'Arise, Sir Kreemy Knut!'

He was smiling under his moustache, his eyes twinkling. I had a sudden and unexpected sensation of purgation, of initiation.

'You're a rather small chap, Woolf.'

'Yes, sir.'

'You're a good 'un all the same. Don't be such a juggins as to find yourself here again, that's all.'

After that he nearly always addressed me as Sir Kreemy Knut, because, I suppose, of my starveling structure. But I never felt that flexible wopper across my trousers again. I faked my way through a minimum of homework, just enough to get away with it. My pain barrier was a low one.

My new hybrid bicycle was a Godsend. I spread my wings: there opened up before me a new and independent world. In the term following Christmas, I actually rode to London. It wouldn't be possible these days, of course, with the juggernaut and the casual cruelty of the present-day King Dick, His Majesty the Consumer, in his fuel-injected fellow assassin. As a matter of fact I took fright at Hounslow. Everthing looked very big, very busy and the stink of exhaust made me dizzy. Not only that, but transport lorries were nearly as formidable as today's, for many of them were chain-driven, and the thought of getting caught up between their immense cog and driving-chain was horrific. One lunch-time on Castle Hill I saw an errand-boy do just that. Numb with horror, I fell off my Pilot onto the grass bank, watching the poor lad's body whirled away — literally broken on the wheel. The crowd, when I got to the brow of the Hill, was so dense as to make it impossible to see a thing; but that afternoon, on my way back to school, the entire stretch of road at the arrow-head meeting of Saint Marks and the Bath Road was thickly strewn with sand and a

116

ruffianly-looking boy told me with unction how he had found a severed toe, just before the ambulance went off.

I was thinking of this all the way home from Hounslow and arrived a nervous wreck. Every heavy vehicle had me cowering and shrinking to the grass verge, especially the Foden steam wagons, with their enormous loads of bricks, and their belching funnels.

And so to Peter Timberlake, but first I feel it necessary to tell how things stood between Muriel and me.

It was in Kings Street that we met when we did meet, and that was only on a Wednesday, when school was out early, in order to allow us to watch the first eleven match on Big Side. Woodrough and Co were heavily down on me, and on all the malcontents who preferred to shog off home to suffering the boredom of the exploits of the muddied oafs at the goal. Timberlake, Monty Hughes (his father kept one of the boathouses at Bray) and a bigger chap called Habits from Knowle Hill, sneaked out by way of Ludlow Road, keeping our heads well down, as we dodged by the Big Side fence, to disperse our various ways. Thus I generally ran into Muriel and Brenda on their way to the Station for their early train. Once or twice I stopped for a natter, but it was not long before I couldn't be bothered even to do that. Both girls had forgiven me my treachery. In fact, my translation to County Boys had given me a prestige which made me oddly shy of them. To be frank, for a little while I felt myself drawn more towards the severe Brenda, whose personality was certainly more incisive than her friend's. We were at an age when one grows quickly. Muriel's elfin charm suffered intensely. She was plumper in no time, and taller. It was Brenda who, in comparision, looked the daintier of the two. She was also the more voluble. She seemed to have played the vampire on poor Muriel: to have sucked at her gaiety and charm; to have reduced her to a quiet, shy creature, who just stared at me in a mumchance, even stupid, way that made me think of one of my uncle's heifers on his farm at Mulbarton in Norfolk. Before long I ceased to stop altogether, continuing with a vague wave of the hand and the smile of Iscariot. Even when she came to the very edge of the pavement to cry out: 'Hello, Hubert!' I went pedalling on. It was a wonder she didn't give up trying altogether. Two years were to slide by, before I was brought to realize how subtly she had magicked Kings Street for me, from Grubbs, the frowzy looking furniture and removal establishment, to Grinstead's the fishmonger next door to the Wesleyan School: from Madame Sprattley, the corstetière, to the Bell Hotel on the corner of Queen Street, where ferns hung down in jungle fashion, and there was an occasional *thé dansant*. Then hindsight revealed the touchingly beseeching manner in which her eyes (and I never ceased to grant them their beauty) rested upon me as I went pedalling by with repulsive insouciance, the little touches she had given her appearance to attract me to her again, the manner with which she tried, though seldom, to exhibit an indifference to me she would regret the moment I was out of sight.

But here is a strange thing. There came times, notably when experiencing an especially delectable phenomenon of the senses, when she swam to the upper level of my consciousness, and shone there like a star. Take as an example the first time I heard Debussy's *The Girl With The Flaxen Hair*. It might, I thought, have been especially composed with Muriel in mind. I saw her, strolling upon a shore in Brittany — I had never been there, but that's where it was in my vision — her blonde locks standing up as if to tangle with the curling clouds, her form returned to its slenderness, drifting along the strand while, in the distance, great layered cliffs lowered, green downland shone with blinding out-croppings of chalk where sheep grazed. Alas, my vision was of a thoroughly idealised Muriel. When I next met her crossing the corner of Grenfell Road, she was just the rather less than mundane, slightly chubby school-kid I had got used to seeing; hat given a slightly original twist, shouldered satchel exaggerating the new amplitudes of her breast, and a high colour indicative of rude health and a good appetite. Where, I wondered, was the pixie who had so captivated me a short time ago?

But Timberlake — what a broth of a boy it was! Sturdy, malicious, fiendishly funny, his face was, without the rotundity, that of Tweedledum robbed of his rattle. Laughing or weeping, his teeth were a piano keyboard, and I recall him as the only person I ever knew whose tears, whether of rage or sorrow, truly gushed from beneath his eyelids. He lived alone with his mother in a miniscule flat at the top of a house facing Station Approach, consisting of one large room and a Lilliputian kitchen. I loved the odd little place. When night came and they hung up a big curtain to make a bedroom for Peter, I often wondered how pretty little Flora Timberlake felt, with the face of the Jubilee Clock gawping in on her, and sometimes the moon as well! They were a lonely pair. Peter was not a popular boy. His temper could be appallingly violent. He was a born anarchist. What he really needed was a papa to beat the little occasional hell out of his backside. But papa had taken himself off, and a divorce ensued. Hence the loneliness of their situation. So long ago there was a prevalence of witches: aged, leaden-nailed old besoms with flat, pinkish wenns, disappearing into the sterile depths of their modesty vests. They had the nailbox out at the first allusion to poor Flora.

For almost three years Peter and I were like David and Jonathan, until one day, apropos of a mere nothing, Flora out and called me a little rat, and all because I had innocently vaunted Pa's skill with his fists. How was I to know that the subject of fathers was a tender one — even taboo. But all the same I was no longer *persona grata* at her home. It didn't worry me much at the time, because I had made a terrific break-through as a pianist: wedding a new lyricism to an already diabolic technique. The few people to whom I played foresaw a future for me, as did my wonderful teacher, Mrs Alice Bales in Pennystone Road.

I had also started fencing at the Drill-Hall. I had, as you might say, put myself under a pretty severe discipline and with a vengeance.

What drew Timberlake and me together in the first place was our mutual hatred of the Head's sons. Bloods, blades, heroes in spotless white flannels and heraldic blazers, who hogged the tennis courts and treated their Father's pupils with terrific hauteur, they rendered us acutely ashamed of our uncouth boots and youthful inelegance. They were, to make things worse, most strikingly handsome. They were regular-featured as young Greek gods crowned, like their Father with crisp dark curls. Would I, I yearned, ever look like them, even remotely? Of course, we only saw them during vacation-time. They were both at Oxford. I sometimes wonder if they, too, became school-masters eventually. If so they would have a long way to go to become as good as their sire.

Then a particular event showed what a startling contrast existed between Peter and me. It was the matter of our first wopping. Mine I have already described. Decorous, even courtly, it left me feeling initiated, belonging — even a trifle distinguished.

One Friday afternoon, on Parade, marching and counter-marching about the new Desborough playing-fields, I was aware all at once of a rattling and tangling of rifle-barrels and, looking back, perceived Peter to be pulling the most extraordinary faces while a tumultuous frothing covered his chin. At the same time, histrionically staggering, he was shoving his fellow 'swaddies' in all directions. At last he fell to the ground, rolling and convulsing dithyrambically. Sergeant Glass wasn't taken in for a moment. He'd seen too many scrimshankers coming the old soldier. Under guard, Timberlake was marched to the Head's study. There was no urbanity about what followed. Damage to the honour of the school; imperilling of the Lucas Tooth trophy . . . Timbers got the works. Six of what I had had. He came out of the Head's house like a shot from a musket, menacing heaven with both fists, his eyes squirting hot, angry tears. He shouted:

'That bugger's dam' near murdered me!' And galloped for the gateway. Nobody made any attempt to prevent his going, but the entire School, by now drawn up in the Quad, burst forth in cruel laughter. Even the uniformed masters chewed at their moustaches: kindly ones like six-foot Dicky Richards and husky Peter Wrench were unable to resist the spectacle of that fire-cracker of a boy, with his furiously scarlet face, from which dried sherbet still floated away on the breeze. At the gates he turned, shook his fist in defiance of the world, arranged his fingers in a rude gesture and tramped off across the Golf Links, totally disregarding the 'No Trespassing' notice, howling *La Marseillaise* at the top of his lung-power - and in perfect French too.

By this time Ma had bought her tea-shop. Like the ancient Athenians, always whoring after some new thing, she was in the seventh heaven of novelty. Coming down Station Approach, I perceived Timberlake, perched perilously at their little gabled window, his tongue fully extended in my direction, thumbing his nose with both hands. Laughing, I crossed over to the Clock Tower and shouted quietly: 'Come and have a cupatea with Ma, old chap.'

He pulled a rueful face. 'I can't' he said.

'Why not?'

'Because that bastard's tanned the arse off my breeks. It's the only pair I've got. They'll run me in!'

'Put your mac on then.'

'That's an idea!' He disappeared and soon came rumbling down the stairs, enveloped in his mother's rain-coat. 'I hocked mine t' other day,' he said carelessly. 'Do I look a pratt?'

'You look fine,' I lied. 'And look . . . there were lots of us didn't laugh, you know. Eddie Lakeman for one.'

He flashed his mad, bad, dazzling smile. 'Forget it,' he scoffed, 'I have. Let 'em laugh. I was always a clown. It'll do their constipation a world of good.' He was a mercurial little fire-brand if ever there was one. But it must have cost him torment to squash his mangled chops on to one of ma's rush-bottomed chairs.

To Victor and me Ma's tea-shop and its heterogenous clientele were good for many a laugh, for furtive helpings of ourselves to the best quality chocolates — Milk Tray had recently come into production and how they excelled the drearily standardised products of today! — and for the cheerful bustle of its situation below Brunel's tall embankment, on the opposite side of Station Approach. There was, for a start, the ceaseless background of steam, the various voices of the locomotives, puffing, spitting, hooting or just a slow, peaceful, meditative chuffing, as one stood drinking at the tank with the thick, flexible tube thrust deep into its iron entrails like a ferruginous stomach-pump. Signals clicked, bells rang imperatively, and at intervals an express rocketed shrieking through to the west: *Lady Superior, Taplow Court, Tre Pol* and *Pen* or *The Great Bear*, and others whose names we collected, perched with note-books upon the big five-barred gate in Shoppenhangers Road.

Now Ma was a person of great charm of manner: straight-laced when her family was around her, capable when it was not of what I can only describe as 'expansions.' She was apt, being thus made, to bring upon herself gross misunderstandings of her true temperament, which was actually that of a virtuous, respectable *mère de famille*. One immediate result of her exuberant nature was the swarming around her establishment, when the nearby offices closed for the day, of a flight of hideous, elderly clerks, one of whom, a Mr Evans — Arthur — from Giddy and Giddy, the neighbouring estate agents, became frenziedly enamoured of her, and conceived a venomous hatred of myself on account of the knowing impudence with which I insisted on regarding him, as he hobbled into the place where my brothers and I sat at tea at our little corner table. Less kind than my Headmaster, he christened me 'Young Barnardo,' to which I retorted with, ironically uttered, 'Mr Heavens.' Very tall, he had been strikingly handsome at one time, but, at the age of seventy-five, retained little more to captivate the ladies than a magnificent head of snow-white, crisply-waving hair and the pseudo-aristocratic face of an erudite and successful politician. His hands, moreover, were repulsively deformed by rheumatoid arthritis. A skeleton grasping a tea-cup would have looked less macabre. He insisted on shortening my mother's name to Mrs Woo' with an unspeakably super-annuated leer.

A step or two further up Station Aproach stood Mrs Thompson's Domestic Employment Agency, and from its

By this time Ma had bought her tea-shop (in Station Approach); a respectable mère de famille . . . the taxi-men adored her. So did her offspring — Tony and Victor escort her in 1929.

desiccated interior, their interview over, would issue forth a well-spaced procession of neatly but seedily attired middle-aged women, too elderly to find employment as maid-servants, scarcely responsible enough to fulfill the function of house-keeper, destined, it seemed from their conversation, to find wretchedly insecure anchorages as companions in bowers of linoleum and lace-curtain of women, hardly less seedy than themselves, but endowed by their marginal security with fiendish arrogance and egocentricity. One of these spinsters, a Miss Paise, fastened on Ma like a limpet. It was useless to endeavour to cheer her up; each effort to do so would be met with the words:

'Yes dear, but how would you like *my* little packet?' followed by a renewed and relentless flow of ever-increasing complaint.

Poor Miss Paise. With what a shock did she discover the reverse side of Ma's beguiling charm! In a flash she found herself on the outside looking in, tea-less and rejected, condemned to the 'parrot-house' of Geronimo's — next but one to the exclusive gown-shop of Miss Myra Salter in Queen Street — where the waitresses were sniffy and snappy with impecunious ladies, but who nevertheless expected to be tipped. Once more a bore had brought out the worst in Ma.

The taxi-men from the Rank adored her. She refilled their flasks with tea at fourpence a time, flirted with them harmlessly, looking, even we had to admit, quite snazzy in her flowered, slightly revealing smock. Not one of them but would have lost a fare to mend her a fuse or fettle up the almost chronically defective ice-cream freezer. Mr Heavens endured excruciating pangs of jealousy.

At four-fifteen or thereabouts came her favourites from the County Girls School: sultry-looking Gipsy Wallace, who drove in from Burnham in a trap drawn by a pony called Pickles, whom she put up at the Bell, and Winifred Cox, fair, sensitive and quietly pretty, who one day amazed and elated me by whispering in my ear:

'I do *wish* you were a little bit older!'

It was Timberlake's mother who introduced me to Maidenhead's world of live entertainment. Hitherto, excepting the cinema, it had been Reading for us, and visits to the Palace or the Vaudeville. Pa took us on the train to catch the second house, stuffed us with goodies, and came back after the interval smelling richly of what Grandma referred to as 'Malt Liquors.'

Now that Ma had her shop, the focus of our lives shifted. After a year at County Boys School I mixed less with the kids from our neck of the woods and more with those of the town. The latter boys belonged to East House, and wore a yellow kneb on their school caps. They represented the school's more sportive element, and their territory commenced halfway down Castle Hill, to take in the town itself, and Bridge Street.

Maidenhead had its Hippodrome: a somewhat obscure and unassuming building, tucked away down by Chapel Arches on the floodplain. Performances were sporadic. In the winter season, when the Maidenhead Operatic and Dramatic Society gave its annual show, approach could be hazardous. A tiny man, a sort of attendant troll in a shabby and overwhelming uniform, swung a dim lantern tremulously in darkness or fog crying: 'This way to the Hippodrome! This way to the Hippodrome! Keep to the duck-boards! Mind the water!' in the tone of some mythological attendant indicating the way to Acheron, and warning you to be careful not to fall in the Styx.

With Peter and his charming little mum I saw *The Quaker Girl*, *The Arcadians* and *The Geisha* before our friendship came to its sudden end. The star of them all was the mother of Victor's particular pals, Harold and Bubbles Breakspear, whose father kept the pharmacy in Kings Street, at the door of which I was to take my last leave of Billy Franklin. Mrs Breakspear had formerly been an operatic singer of considerable note before her marriage. Known professionally as Grace Kenza, she continued to be thus billed in her now amateur status. Peter and I had a real cult for her, especially in her role of *The Geisha*. Her saucy oriental make-up enchanted us. We went around warbling *The Goldfish* song for weeks. She still gave singing lessons at their house in the Crescent where, when at last we became acquainted, she offered me the use of her magnificent white Blüthner to practice on. She just could not understand why I steadfastly declined to play in public, and I was unable to give her a reasonable explanation.

Then there were the Odds And Ends: a happy little concert-party which took the Hippodrome for an occasional week. I always found myself listening for the ebb and flow of waters beneath, it was all so reminiscent of a summer show on the pier. A lovely big girl, a super principal-boy type, I vividly and amorously recall, not born, not made — but BUILT; that was her. Her name on the bill was Beatrice Mayne. The comic, Chris Weed, I subsequently met when I went into show business myself. He was marvellous, both as laughter-maker and human-being.

The Panto was frankly shabby and third-rate. Where they dug up the ham-fats to play in it, God knows! We always saw the one at the Vaudeville Theater in Broad Street, Reading, taking my paternal Granny, who was a perfect darling. A widow, for many years she had kept pro's digs in the Town, in Southampton Street. She was the perfect type of 'Ma' in a long, severe buttoned dress with a stiff, high collar, side-curls and a big silver watch pinned to her chest.

Not the least of the season's diversions were the Fourpenny Pops, an incredible mish-mash of local talent organised and run by Mrs Thorne, who lived in Saint Marks Road, not far from the Browns. Tall, full-cheeked, enormously fanged, she sported hats that were miracles of natural history, composed of birds, small beasts and fishes garnished with wheat ears, teazles and a grand gallimaufry of other wonders of nature. Her entertainments took place at our quaint Town Hall. They were usually packed to capacity. Why wouldn't they be? Fourpence wasn't a fortune even for inferior talent, and the Pops were seldom that. Mrs Thorne was no fool. The performers who volunteered their services, singers and instrumentalists of all kinds, were largely of that vast category of entertainers, sometimes all too justly, occasionally rather bitchily styled 'Artistes Manquées': sopranos who warbled over-passionately the songs of Tosti, pulsating contraltos who sonorously gargled *Softly Awakes* by Saint Saëns, baritones who rumbled and boomed Kipling's *Boots* or *The Arethusa* .

126

Most of them suffered, I suppose, from the unmistakeable flaws resulting from inferior teaching, or just that melancholy shortfall of talent. The comics were customarily so frightfully bad as to be frightfully good. Mrs Thorne never really forgave me for refusing to sacrifice my own talent as accompanist to her over-sensitive, insecure, tetchy amateurs.

Tony, Mother, Victor and, on the right, Harold Breakspear, (son of Grace Kenza, the singer), whose father kept the pharmacy in Kings Street. She gave singing lessons in the Crescent.

To my mind the truly superior show of the winter season was the one put on by the County Girls School, also at the Town Hall. One of the mistresses, Miss Russel, was a really first-rate musician, who contrived to get together from among the senior girls and her fellow-teachers a creditable orchestra. For the first time in my experience there glimmered excitingly from the orchestra pit, lights on music-stands, half revealing individuals known to me but glamorously unfamiliar in evening-dress. There followed a quite unanticipated parade of talent — even a display of genuine gifts. Renee's friend, Gracey Clere, gave an exquisite *pas seul*, a ballet of a graceful Victorian miss caught in a shower of rain and obliged to perform sinuous manoeuvres with her pink parasol. She brought the house down and gave an encore. Then Dorothy

Upson, daughter of the corner chemist hardby, redeemed a spectacled dumpiness, and looked quite pretty in a duet from *Veronique* with Gracey's big sister, Doreen. A year or two later she wrote and published a few novels, which are now well out of print, more's the pity. Miss Russel's taste was fastidious. She conducted the time-honoured *Hockey Song* without much enthusiasm, but with wonderful quiet brio a unison song of her own composition: a Chinese thing in which the girls were enchantingly beautiful in oriental costumes and make-up. This number took the form of a long string of Chinese place-names to a melodiously subtle accompaniment. It was a trifle Delius-derived, but who was there to notice that? The girls swung Chinese lanterns, and performed a few sinuous steps, as they sang this really very cleverly composed song, modulating, rather nostalgically from major to minor and back again.

I carried away from that particular evening two widely different sets of impressions: firstly, the group of entr'actes consisting of Debussy's *Arabesques* and that delectably evocative composition, *Valse De La Reine* by Coleridge Taylor, and secondly, the spectacle of the caddish Penn, whose father kept the bookshop in King Street, being frog-marched out by four muscular attendant Boy Scouts, for having hurled, in petty exasperation, a rotten pear across the hall, demolishing the best hat of a harmless and inoffensive old lady.

The entr'actes went, needless to say, straight into the Muriel song-book, and that despite the fact that I had not seen or thought of her for ages. She was, in fact, treasure I was unconsciously hoarding.

11

Down Town Blues

Ma, having disposed of her little tea-dive, returned with joy to hedonistic pursuits. My contemporaries and I were three years older, up in the Lower Fifth, our voices almost through the cuckoo-stages, some of us cloaking beneath a callow chicken-down, neon-like boils and pimples.

In September I got the shock of my life. Muriel went abroad, and I was suddenly cast in the role of adolescent widower. It was a tragic-comic situation.

I heard of it from the willing lips of Brenda, two days after taking Grandma to see *Flames Of Passion*. Well might I have been ravished by the splendour of Muriel's legs as she stood in the ballet third position, the basket of figs in her hands, chatting to Sue Hunt in the soft September sunshine. Well might I have resolved upon a reconquest of her affections! Who will not, when he may, when he will shall have nay! Brenda reported her departure with, I considered, unnecessary glee. Muriel had had a return of bronchial trouble, and been dispatched to some relations who owned a villa in Marrakesh!

Marrakesh! . . . so distant in those far-off days: so exotic, so disquietingly alien. It might have been to the Hills Of The Chankley Bor or to The Great Grombulian Plain that they had transported her. I was unexpectedly stunned. It truly was a psychic pole-axing. I went off my food and my fencing. How crass the ridiculous ritual of the latter in face of my horrible loss! For days I forgot the piano. Music unmanned me distressingly. Only the melodies of the Muriel Song Book glided up like lovely ghosts to haunt me. *Valse De La Reine*, *La Fille Aux Cheveux De Lin*, *What'll I do*? What'll I do, indeed!

I took to endless wandering, alternating beauty with squalor. I smoked like a navvy. I saw more of Maidenhead during her three months absence than ever before. I saw without warning the spikes beneath the roses and, with fearful clarity, became aware of rust-eaten corrugated iron fences, broken glass on walls, nails that climbing urchins drove into elm trees, decaying rooks self-slain by collision with leafy boughs. Often I viewed with sour repulsion the concrete walls of the town's poorer quarters, like East Street, shedding their facings like dead dinosaurs their skins: sprouting straggly growths of charlock and snap-dragon strays, like posthumously growing hair.

Autumn came on. Daily I waited at our green front gate for a letter — even a post-card — from her; thinking all the time: why should she, after years of insultingly casual neglect?

How I came to hate the daily-breaders on their way to work, stuffy Mr Baker in his too-small straw hat, Mr Appleyard in his awful pride, Mr Ashley, so soon to die of tuberculosis at Peppard, and Leslie Cartware, now a reformed character and a leading light in the Salvation Army. As the postman, Mr Coleman, went by without even a sign, I could have shot him in the back, knocked off the ridiculous little Ruritanian foot-soldiers' kepi that postmen then wore.

Then one or the other of the Jacobs would come out and ask me if I'd heard from that little tart of mine yet: espcecially Aleric, the eldest, who was a clever sadist, hinting at all sorts of temptations waiting to befall a pretty blonde in the souks and posh hotels of the desert interior.

Autumn came on. Sunday morning from our front-room window, I regarded the chestnut leaves slowly drifting and curvetting down, the pools forming when it rained heavily, where the drain was chronically blocked at the lamp-post's foot, and the people parading dimly and drearily to Church to the clamour of the bells: the Appleyards from Courthouse Road, consumed with pride; Mr Heavens, who lodged in Spencer Road, eaten up by his late flowering lust, and variously afflicted geriatrics in their bath-chairs, clutching with spiky fingers at the steering-handles, peering eerily from side to side of their vehicles with glaucous eyes, like hermit-crabs from their adopted shells. One ancient lady, too infirm to guide herself in her creaking chariot, was both pushed by a pretty, young relation and dragged by a scruffy boy. Her lips were spotted purple, trembled like some insect-consuming orchid, and she gave vent to a periodic, singularly ghastly and protracted chuckle. I thought fleetingly of living to be like that, and quickly took refuge from such a horrendous idea in youth's merciful resilience.

Sunday afternoons, to kill time, I made crude experiments in what later came to be called Social Observation. From the sordidness of Moffat Street, with its black-aproned, draggled matrons trotting over cracked pavements, clutching their jugs of dinner-ale, in broken boots and men's cloth-caps, fixed by lethal-looking hat-pins, I made my way up to Gringer Hill by way of Marlow Road, Crawfurd Rise and the railway arch. Here there was still the faint scent of late roses. The Victorian mass of Crawfurd College towered on my left, while on my right glimmered the rugger-posts of St Piran's, a fantastically chic cannister-stuffer.

Further on, still on the right, stood back majestically the even more exclusive cramming establishment of Dr Oldershaw. He had a terrific reputation for tutoring. His students consisted chiefly of the sons of nobles and nabobs without, it was said, much up top. A Woosterian academy, you might say . . . an international one.

At the gates the Japanese Prince, Mirauki, and a suave young Egyptian both superfinely suited, reclined in a white Issoto Fraschini lined with scarlet leather, chatting-up the Gascoigne sisters, stunning in the black and white-striped blazers of Elmsleigh House School. Both had exquisitely shingled blue-black hair, with fringes and a sable scimitar at each cheek. Their eyes were violet-blue: their stockings, of white cotton, unbelievably fine and elegant. In vain I strove to summon up a burning indignation at the staring contrast between the reeking squalor of Moffat Street and this tranquil oasis of Maidenhead's choicest suburb, where breathed, if I may borrow his phrase, what Scott Fitzgerald had described as 'an air of cheerful snobbery.' All I could call up was a portrait of Muriel: her almond eyes, peach skin and warm-blonde hair, that she could arrange in such a bewildering variety of styles. And those legs of hers! Under date-palms, mosques and minarets I pictured her. Sinister faces turned to leer after her with unutterable concupiscence as she went by. I smelt Turkish coffee, flower-scented dust, the cold air breathing in from the desert as the sun set in the sultry, glamorous blaze. My adolescent fancy painted fantastically lurid pictures . . . Her slanting eyes above a yashmak: she the favourite of the harem: the heaped dishes of cous-cous, the silvery fountains, the sherbet, the narghile, the burnished bangles, the shrilly congested cadences of reed pipes and the trilling, out of swoony blue shadows, of the amorous voice of the Bul-Bul.

Pursued by such self-conjured nightmares, I went home by way of Linden Avenue, then not adopted by the Council: a wonderfully convenient place for the no-hopers from the Workhouse to brew up, rich with wild flowers all summer long. There I ran into Big-Boy Baker who, by a lucky chance, was in a hurry, and paused just long enough to heave me into the ditch.

And I thought, staring up the noble length of our Avenue with its ghastly Cemetery to my right and, half a mile away, the relatively pleasant Churchyard of All Saints, what a setting for a really spectacular funeral in the Parisian grand-manner: coal black prancers and plumes and miles of flowing crêpe, and silver-teared fringes adorning sable palls. Our generation was just about seeing out those grand obsequies, just as we were the last to go to bed by candle-light.

12

The Old Tea Shop

One frosty after-Christmas morning, sandwich and thermos-provided, I walked out to Hawthorne Hill. So nippy it was that you were better on your feet than a bicycle. I'd got a silly little tune running through my brain, and so I found myself stepping out to it up Bray-wick Road.

'Tap tap rap rap in the lonely mountain gap
All night long from dark to dawn
Busy little Leprechaun.'

It was number one in the Muriel Song Book. I have an idea that its composer and lyric-writer were both Miss Mayne. When we warbled it in the playroom to her jaunty accompaniment, we were just eight. Muriel had had some scented beads for Christmas, and I plagued her endlessly to fish them out, warm from her bosom, for me to smell. As she tucked them back, she smiled up at me from under her blonde lashes, sleepily, conspiratorially. She never got irritated or bored with this, my earliest manifestation of boyish sensuality.

I ate my sandwiches in the cleft of a cut hat-stack and sipped my hot, sweet tea. The frost had persisted all morning and now perched upon the twigs an inch thick — grey but startlingly candid in contrast with the leaden sky. I snoozed for a bit. The hay made a little oven around me. In the middle of the field lay a plough on its side, defeated by the iron sod. I hadn't thought much of Hawthorne Hill. It was the wrong season: no Household Cavalry steeple chases; no flat-bellied Royal Daimlers; no purple-faced, boozy Prince of Wales rolling about in his saddle like last year, falling off twice and yet being allowed to win. Uninspired as yet by the bewitching presence of Mrs Simpson, it might be supposed. Stiffly I returned homeward.

Drifting and dreaming I came at last to the Jubilee Clock. It said three o'clock. Dusk was early; mingled gas and electric lights twinkled in the shops. I glanced up and thought how long it seemed since the Timberlakes had departed. I crossed from the railway arch and turned into Grenfell Road. Pomeroys had begun frying. My taste buds awoke. From the newsagent a policeman led a foxy-looking little man by the arm. I remembered him from Ma's tea-shop days. A bookie's runner. How many times had he been led off to the violently red brick lock-up in the Broadway?

Outside the Temperance Hotel two shabby men started a half-hearted scrap. One took a dirty fist plumb in the face and went off howling dismally. The poor devil, I casually speculated, had never come out of anything but the little end of the horn! His wobbly gait spoke of anything but temperance.

It was at the Park gate that I got this mysterious and elating sense of premonition. An instant change came over that portion of Maidenhead's landscape: not a momentary one either, but an absolute transformation of identity that completely altered the character of our rapport. It had little or nothing to do with the subtlety of early winter twilight, drifting across the silver-grey bareness of beech-boles; was entirely unconnected with the white, frost-carpeted sweep of the playing fields, stretching like a frozen lake beneath the vast amphitheatre of beech and fir. As well ascribe this ecstatically bizarre sensation to the delicious but mundane aroma of cod, rock-salmon and chipped potatoes drifting from Pomeroys' door into the increasingly frigid airs of the January afternoon, or the shrill but muted shriek of a schoolmaster's whistle calling his grubby flock in from the fields.

Without toil, a blister on my heel forgotten, I went up the steep and icy paths between the trees, through the iron gate, across Southill Road and, under the close-growing conifers of the Fir Walk and came face to face with Muriel!

She hurried and looked bothered, but the second she recognized me, a look of such intense pleasure and relief irradiated her face, so that my legs almost failed me and my heart did a flip-flap.

"Fernley."

(TELEPHONE: **709** Maidenhead.)

Resident Pupils for University, Bar and Service Examinations.

PRINCIPAL:

LUCIAN OLDERSHAW,

M.A., J.P.

Expert Individual Tuition by Resident and Visiting Staff.

TESTS AND REPORTS FOR ALL EXAMINATIONS.

TERMS, REFERENCES and SUCCESSES
::   ON APPLICATION   ::

The even more exclusive cramming establishment of Dr Oldershaw . . . students . . . without, it was said, too much up top. A Woosterian academy.

'Oh, Hubert,' she gasped. 'Its you! really and truly you! I can't believe it! Thank God you're here!'

She rushed forward and took my hands between her own, squeezing them hard. She looked fearfully back over her shoulder 'There,' she exclaimed. 'I was always all right with you, wasn't I? Look, he's running off now he's seen you!'

My gaze followed hers. In the ever-deepening dusk a shambling something was dodging away towards Castle Hill, taking advantage, or imagining he did, of the slender young trees. I knew him at once.

'It's only old Monkey-Man!' I reassured her, 'He won't hurt you. He's as harmless as a dove — though he's not much like one to look at.'

'You could easily have fooled me,' she said.

For a short space we clasped each other's hands. We looked into each other's eyes and the years fell away. Lingeringly we kissed . . . .

'An hour ago.' I whispered, 'I just wouldn't have dared.'

'Imbecile,' she replied in a shaky voice, 'you'd have been dearly welcome any time since we were kids together. I've always adored you, love.'

I was suprised to catch tears in her eyes. I would have expected a deep sun-tan. Instead her Nordic fairness remained untinged by the African sun. The brisk air had coloured her rather chubby cheeks. On her shingled hair a tiny grey beret impudently perched. Belted by a common luggage-strap, an Afghan leather hunting-coat clasped her waist tightly; stood up around her ears. Well-cut shoes of brown suéde, plainly laced, accentuated the sinuous grace of her dancer's feet.

The riding wind soughed in the fir-tops. Flakes of frost drifted down like the ghosts of still-born babies. She shivered suddenly, shrinking back into her coat. 'Darling,' she gulped, 'I'm cold! I got to hate Morrocco but it's certainly warmer there. Can't we go and get a cup of tea somewhere in the warm and chat and just look at one another?'

And what do you think we found when we sat down in ma's old tea-shop? In a Dolly Varden get-up, very posh and hoity-toity, the somewhat elderly waitress stood, grimacing demurely, chit-book and pencil poised. There was something more than vaguely familiar about her, I thought; squinting in the dim, religious light.

'Tee, peestries, strawbrah ace?' she inquired.

It was Miss Paise. She looked well, despite her rather random make-up, and appeared to have discovered her niche.

Muriel had been to lunch with Miss Burn to discuss her future studies. She had, I noticed at once, developed a neat volubility very much at variance with her former rather tattily charming flow. She too had been under discipline.

Her aunt in Marrakesh, an extremely important theatrical agent, had taken her in hand, sharpening up her personality, bullying her out of her too-ready inclination to tears as a first reaction to rebuke or criticism, sending her to a school of music and drama, conducted by an elderly Russo-Algerian, whom Muriel described as an old bat out of Hades. Now she had been enrolled at the Vera Varconi School at Slough, where she was to attend four mornings a week. Hence the interview with Miss Burn, who was so deeply charmed by her beautiful pupil that she was inclined to grant her whatever she asked.

'It's wonderful — absolutely wonderful!' she exclaimed, digging her fork into a third pasty. 'I'm only to do one morning a week at school and four afternoons. What's more I'm to get around by myself more. Aunt Laura says I've been too coddled all my life. Do you know, Hubert, dear, I've scarcely been to a birthday party in my life? It was always a question of my lungs.' She drew her Afghan coat apart. 'Do I look as if there was anything wrong with my lungs?'

I felt my eyes spring open.

'Why, my darling, you're shy! How lovely! do you know, a little Turkish lady came up to me at one of Aunt Laura's parties and asked me if she might teach me to do the *Danse du Ventre* — you know — the Belly Dance. I told her I wouldn't mind and she gave me a little pinch and said "Mademoiselle a bien de quoi!" Flattering, eh?'

'Salacious old cow!'

'Not a bit. She was paying me a great compliment. They really go for a bit of sticky-out plumpness in those regions. Don't you?'

A new Muriel, this! I was about to change the subject when she leaned forward and said:

'And now I think it's about time you called me by the name I get at home. It's Mooghie. Soppy, I dare say, but that's the only way I could get it out as a baby and it's stuck, you know.'

I drew in my breath. 'But it's charming.' I said. 'Why didn't you tell me about it before? It's got sort of Oriental overtones to it. It's sort of Art Nouveau. It's absolutely you!'

She blushed like a rose. 'How lovely. I'm so glad you like it. It's worried me a bit for quite a long time.'

'Mooghie,' I asked. 'What are you going to do with all this new freedom?'

'Work,' she replied, 'and dance and practice my guitar like mad. The mad Mooghie. Perhaps I'll be billed like that.'

'I think that will suit you very well.'

'And in between times I'll have lovely assignations with you in the Fir-Walk. I have no belief at all in his harmlessness, that Monkey-Man of yours. I was always alright with you, wasn't I, Hubert?'

'And are you really going on the stage like — like Winnie Shotter?'

'No, not like her at all. I'm going for cabaret and revue at first — ultimately musical comedy, I hope. Laura says I should keep personal recitals in mind, but I'm not altogether sure about that. I must just see how my voice goes on. Actually it's a sort of a cross between a jew's harp and a day-old chick. I don't think much of it myself. But what about you, my darling? So mature and noble of feature.' She looked more closely. 'Not a single pimple either! That's lovely! You ought to see Dennis Brierly. All lumps and bumps and woolly fluff! Like a lustful verger, Daddy says.' Suddenly she narrowed her eyes. 'By the way, what did you mean by cutting me dead and cutting off just before I went off to foreign parts. But for that I'd have sent you a post-card or two — you know . . . X marks my room . . . wish you were here. But I thought: damm him to Hell.

The Pamela Tea Rooms

(L. A. WOODS, Proprietor)

See our windows for the finest selection of

Fancy Cakes and Pastries

at a most reasonable price, all made on the premises

UNDER PERSONAL SUPERVISION

Light Luncheons and Afternoon Teas a Speciality

Wedding and Birthday Cakes made to order

Our Keynote is VALUE

45 Queen Street MAIDENHEAD

(Opposite Police Station)

Pamela and Doris maintained the twenties tradition of the local tea-shop: 'Tee, peestries, strawbrah ace?'

"DORIS"

6 Bridge Street   ::   Maidenhead

(Close to Cinemas)

For DAINTY TEAS and REFRESHMENTS

Cream Ices a Speciality

CHOCOLATES
All Best Makes

CIGARETTES and TOBACCOS
All well-known Brands in stock

— *Agency for Workers* —

You were coming from the Rat-Palace in Queen Street and I was buying figs from Sue Hunt. And that dear little old lady with you . . . you were shoving her along like a pram, poor old love. So rough!'

'My grandmama . . . I just didn't want you to meet her. She's not a bit of a dear old lady. Just an old Norfolk rat-bag who considers Maidenhead as a sort of Sodom and Gommorha. But, my dear, if I had known you were off next day she might have tramped home by herself. If you must know, it was only on the way home with her that I realized how much you meant to me, Mooghie.'

'And what brought that on?'

'Your legs,' I said with crude simplicity.

She got up and stretched her arms, yawning unashamedly.

'Are you busy at anything tomorrow, Hubert, love?'

'Rather not.'

'Then how do you fancy taking me to see *Way Down East*—that is if you care for Lilian Gish. I adore her. Do say you will.'

'Of course I will. But I see shadows of the darkest kind ahead. What happens when you go off to show business? What becomes of me?'

The smile she gave me was one of genuine determination.

'You'll come with me,' she said. Her voice was as quiet and certain as when she was a small, quiet, certain little girl. 'What else? And what on earth were you thinking about to let me gorge all those lovely cakes? Look: I can barely do up my belt! I'm going to end with my bosom down to my knees. Then I'll have *trop de quoi*, won't I? — and look, my train goes out in five minutes. I'd put it off but daddy will be waiting for me at Cygnet Halt . . . '

As the train pulled out from the dimly lit platform she kissed me as if without a care in the world.

'Tomorrow, then, at three by the Clock Tower,' she said softly.

'I love you, my darling.' Then she drew back and closed the window. I felt very flat and solitary as the tail-light disappeared, but the clanking of the milk-churns was like a celebratory peal of bells. I did wonder about the drying-up of my scant hoard of Christmas money. Perhaps I'd do a paper round for Mr Brown.

13

Miss Burn's Young Lady

Miss Mary Burn . . . The very sound of her name is an excavator plunging into the vitals of my past. It brings up a vision of richly towering rhododendrons in the County Girls School drive, especially the white ones with their amazing dark stamens clustering within the grey shadow at the floral, fleshy heart. Collin's White, I believe they were called. From the toad-stooly, beech-masty-smelling drive, haunted in the evening by hedgehogs, they cascaded out towards the tennis courts as if desperately avid for the sunshine burnishing every grass-blade.

Miss Burn was a disciplinarian, but a benevolent one. Her rules were made to be observed. Let a parent keep her child from school for some family junketting — for example a wedding — without due notice, and Mary Burn was Nemesis! Her pleasant, comfortable study overlooking the gardens became, for the summoned parents of the truant, a dragon's lair, struck terror into the soul of the most arrogant of them. They wilted, stammered and fell into pitiable states of woolly apology beneath the hanging-judge mumur of her voice. Then Miss Burn revived them with tea and biscuits and the most incredible charm. Thence-forth they spoke of her with bated breath and in terms of fervid admiration. Their offspring became models of punctuality and brought flowers. Conversely she would accede without hesitation to a letter of polite request and, if it should be a beautifully expressed missive, she walked among us at playtime, perusing it with pleasure, emitting great gusts of her full-throated, equine laughter.

The School stood back behind a spacious, gravelled rotunda. It resembled a country seat more than a mere secondary school. Trees concealed it massively from the outside world. At its summit, like a funny hat from a cracker, squatted a small chamber of coloured glass to which we climbed for our annual medical examination. This, of course, was before we little 'uns moved across to our new quarters at Queen Anne House at the beginning of 1918.

In Summer there was a garden-party on Speech-Day. An excessively grand affair. Then Miss Burn was truly in her full glory. She circulated regally among her assembled guests, her great straw picture-hat rearing above them, her dove-grey silk gown flowing and billowing around her however still and clement the atmosphere, her double strapped shoes tottering over the sweetly bruised grass. In spite of her many eccentricities she excited little mirth, most parents being quite terrified of her overpowering presence. Even her wonky pince-nez sat astride her proud, fleshy nose with all the dread authority of orb or sceptre. Her girls wore horrible indigo knickers almost to their knee-caps. Their gym-slips' bodices were pleated to conceal to the ultimate pitch of development their mammary embonpoint. And it was: 'Yes Miss Burn — no Miss Burn — three bags full, Miss Burn' all the way. And, *mirabile dictu*, all was achieved by kindness joined to total belief in her own sense of personal majesty.

Poor Mary Burn . . . In a few short years she died, quite mad, in an asylum for the insane: her glorious authority shredded to ruin in a maelstrom of utter confusion and lunatic nattering. There are times when I find myself wondering what she would have made of her dear, cherished establishment become a youth club — smooching and pot in the dark caves of the rhododendrons; fierce snarling of electronic music with the thwacking eternity of paganistic drumming in the former assembly-hall; the police summoned almost regularly to quell a punch-up.

All too recently the very landscape has been bulldozed, destroyed by that barbaric iron tear-drop swinging from a crane. Had she lived it would have been to see in all its violent ugliness the destruction of Queen Anne, the shops in the immediate vicinity and an immense and scaring roundabout

142

Miss Mary Burn was a disciplinarian with a sense of majesty. At the St Andrew's Fancy Dress Party in the Hall, she presided — in the centre of her charges, who included Peggy Bar, Miss White, Miss Alice Russell, Miss Richmond, Olga -----, ----- Symmonds, Brenda Blatford, Alice Ireland, Miss Adams, Stella Collins, Dorothy Bartholomew, Mabel Wakeling, Annie Bradley, Eileen Smith and Ruby Bush.

extending as far as Kidwells Park. I imagine that ghastly iron tear bashing and smashing into those walls that so gently sheltered my early childhood: shattering wall and ceiling; revealing to vulgarly curious eyes shreds and patches of familiar wallpapers, and all the obscenity of the slaughterman's knife as the animals' guts roll and slither out.

One Sunday evening on the 'box' I watched *Sunday Half-hour* from Maidenhead's Wesleyan Chapel. I haven't got over it yet. A shot from a 'chopper' showed me the extent of the planner's triumph at the bottom of Castle Hill.

We met three times a week. I used to lurk behind one of the brick pillars of the Fir Walk gate until she was half way up to me, in order to avoid for us both the embarrassment of meeting near the sozzling stench of the noisome gents' convenience, wedged between the Walk and the School.

Now if there was one terrestrial phenomenon Miss Burn abhorred above this offence to nose and eye, it was the person of Monkey-Man. Kind and gentle Christian as she was, I believe that if, by an effort of will, she could have pulverized both loo and loony, the latter without pain, she could have watched their dust drift away on our softly prevailing south-west wind with calm philosophy.

When her girls went home at lunch-time, he would post himself somewhere or other on the Hill, sometimes by the castellated flint wall of Castle House, at others on the corner of Grenfell Road even, when his courage was up, directly outside the heavy door giving entrance to the School itself. Somehow, though he was pretty deaf, he had contrived to learn many of the girls' christian names: imperfectly it is true, but comprehensibly.

'K' treeny,' he would mumble and splutter from under his simian upper lip . . . 'Nanancy — Brendy — Nedna!' followed by a stream of mumbo-jumbo, impossible to understand, but all too easy to interpret on account of the unequivocal gestures into which he arranged his fingers. He was taken up by the police once or twice, disappeared for a space, then there he was again, perhaps lurking under the balcony of The Ice House, perhaps beneath the enormous cedar on the slope leading to Castle Hill Terrace — or Doctor's Drive as it was known to us. He was reputed to be quite harmless: 'Quite innocuous,' the school Doctor told Miss Burn. But Miss Burn was sceptical. Could it have been her own approaching insanity that put her on his wavelength?

At all events Mooghie was terrified of him, and most of all at the way he mispronounced her name.

'Moor'el!' he whined: 'Moor'el !'

One afternoon, when he ventured too close to her, I gave him a swishing cut across his back with my foil. He kept clear after that, but I felt my flesh crawl at the look that swam like a rotten fish across his eyes, as he took in her shapely plumpness, the shiny gold of her hair, her dancer's legs.

Now that she was a special pupil Miss Burn permitted her to dress in the same style as the pupil-teachers: in a skirt of navy-blue, a white blouse with a high V-neck and a black bow. She got away with black silk stockings too. In fact, with Miss Burn, she seemed to get away with just anything.

A new, racy fluency with which she expressed herself . . . Did it not suggest a similarly changed moral condition? During her absence in the Middle East I had endured torments of jealousy and distrust. These visions were slow in dissipating. Moreover my reading lent a lurid background to my thoughts. Aldous Huxley and the sophisticated moral turpitude of charaters like Mrs Viveash in *Antic Hay* and Mary Thriplow in *Those Barren Leaves*: Marcel Proust and his perfidious Odette de Crèçy: Flaubert and poor *Madame Bovary* — 'poor' despite her abominable treatment of her selfless but contemptibly idiotic husband . . .

I took to killing time as usefully as possible: wearing it away from one meeting to the next. Those black silk stockings seemed as if they might very well prove to be the death of me.

I was not long in discovering about her virtue.

One Saturday afternoon we went together to the Bridge Street Cinema. It was drizzling a little and the road surfaces starting to glimmer with shiny misery. I thought how abject and louche appeared the second-hand shop of Mrs Horwood just down the street. 'Wardrobes Bought' said her sign, and I wondered by what Jesuitic sophistry a small Catholic Church became deconsecrated and turned into a rag-and-bone emporium. The spire and its cross remained, also its minute belfry. What a tumble from Biggs' Aladdin's cave just up the Street down to Mrs Horwood's slop-shop! The very neatness of her new sign only rendered more cranky and decrepit the Church's vestiges.

In *Eve* and *Everybody's Film Review* I started to undo the buttons of Mooghie's blouse. To my dismay she showed signs of instant and acute distress, not withdrawing from me, but assuming a frozen passivity that was heartbreaking. It was as if I was attempting the violation of the little girl in pink gingham!

'Oh, Hubert, don't — please don't!'

Against my shoulder I felt her shallow, breathing and the rapid pulsing of her heart.

'Sorry,' I whispered. 'Sorry. I thought — '

'Its all right, dear. Don't be upset. I'll be better in a minute — really I will.'

So I contented myself with my arm around her and her head on my shoulder, and after the Pathé *Gazette* came John Barrymore's horrifying performance as *Doctor Jekyll and Mr Hyde*. That had us locked together in grim earnest!

'You've really and honestly forgiven?' I asked her as we sipped our tea. 'I do feel so infernally contrite — I really do! But my darling Mooghie: how was I to know you'd dislike it so?'

She grinned up at me, spearing her fourth éclair. 'Who said I didn't like it?' She said.

'But I thought , it seemed to me — '

'Darling boy, it was lovely but so frightening. So frightening I almost fainted. I've a horror of doing that in a public place. That's why I never went to parties, you see.I'm just beginning to get over it. You'll have to ravish me by degrees. Nobody has ever touched me like that before. I really think I must have liked it only too well!'

'One button at a time, then, you think? — here, you'd better let me finish the éclair for you. You're going chlorotic.'

'What's that, love?'

'Green,' I told her, helping myself.

Miss Paise was getting to know us. 'That'll be three and ninepence, my dears,' she said. 'My goodness you're going to be icky-pooh!'

Gypsy Wallace was mounting her trap. 'Why,' she said; 'it's the Heavenly Twins!' she whipped up Pickles before we really had time to recognize her.

R. MARTIN

47 High Street : MAIDENHEAD

Tel. 644.

FOR

General Drapery & Ladies' & Children's Wear

'Wardrobes Bought' said Miss Horwood's second-hand shop sign: Martins was at the other extreme — Maidenhead's upmarket drapery of the '20s, where Mrs Campbell doubtless bought Mooghie's blouse . . .

147

I looked up at the eye-socket of Mrs Timberlake's old flat. In its curtainless state it looked more abandoned and lonely than ever.

'Do you remember Peter Timberlake, Mooghie?' I asked her.

'Yes, I do, and what a dreadful little toad he was!'

Remembering the merry days letting off steam as a relief from my studies; the cosy teas round his mum's fire and her scrumptious currant cakes, all sugary and crisp round the outer edges, my heart smote me. For a second I regarded Mooghie with mild distaste. And I was already getting used to her paying for our tea half the time, was fast becoming a right young gigolo, parasite and leech.

14

In Grenfell Park

When, before his ennobling in 1905, Lord Desborough gave the piece of land now known as Grenfell Park to the town, the Mayor, old Tom Stuchberry, gave his second son Richard, the job of landscaping it. This was twenty years after Brunel had scooped, as from an enormous Stilton cheese, all the material he required to raise his embankment across the south side of Maidenhead in 1871.

Now, when we were children in the second decade of this present century, the lofty beeches behind the iron railings were over a hundred years old. They dwarfed the Park keeper's lodge and the swings and see-saws of the play-ground and, with the firs planted by Richard Stuchberry, gave an imposing look of Switzerland to the slopes surrounding the playing fields.

Brunel's navvies, in their dinted bowler-hats and chalk-caked corduroys, slaving away in all weathers, skidding in sodden or sun-baked chalk with pick and shovel, horse-goading, straining at wheels sunk in the eternal chalk, had been clearly directed to take good care of the half-grown beeches, and there thus remained, fifty years later, perched high on what, in the American far West, are known as buttes, beeches of gigantic proportions, strangling their chalky supports with massively serpentine roots, up to which it was exciting and romantic to climb. After rain, the hollows and caverns created by so much radical anarchy would fill with refreshingly soft, brown water. It was delicious. As kids, we drank pints of it, afterwards agitating it with a stick to transform it into turbid whiteness — poison for our pursuers.

That winter the Park became a place of enchantment. We

149

used to pause in the gloaming half way down the slope, watching the cloud-shapes in the western sky, holding hands and sniffing the sulphurous air from the railway, the damp, coal-dusty pungency of the tall black heaps in the railway yard, and appetizing odours of toast and high-teas from the nice little terraced railway cottages climbing the left side of Grenfell Road. From their curtained front windows, gas-light twinkled tremulously between leafless branches. When evenings were still and cold, with little wind to torment and drive the clouds, vast battlements of deepest purple built up, sandwiching between their sombre masses wide streaks of cinnabar. Mooghie would sniff deeply at the nutty fragrance of decaying beech-leaves, look from under her slanting eyes at me and say, with a return to pink gingham days:

'Oh, isn't it all lovely!'

Sometimes, when rain dropped cold from grey-washed skies, we hurried through the raw-smelling sub-way and it's heavy door, with brazen, polygonal handle, to find shelter in the covered yard, where the hand-carts were stored, and be kissing before the thunderous reverberation of the slamming door had died away. Frenzied airs whined in the chink of a cracked window, rain dripped in a puddle like a reiterated harp-note in a score by Ravel; in the rigid filigree of pear-tree twigs across in Such's Orchard sang the wind like a concorde of scrannel-pipes.

On one occasion we ran into the Headmaster under the sub-way on his way, I assumed, to Smallbones for an ounce of his favourite Saint Julian. Long gone were the days of my dragooning into the performance of this small but maddening chore. Obviously he had failed to entrap some hapless tadpole between the school and the main gate. He acknowledged my raised cap with absent amenity, observed Mooghie with her rain-spangled honey-blonde hair, blinked at her beauty, and raised his heavy grey homburg with a courtly rather charming little bow.

'What a handsome old gentleman!' she murmured. 'I think he was a bit smitten with me, don't you? How deevy!'

She had taken to employing outmoded Edwardisn slang. Its uses by anyone else would have sounded mushy. She made it cute and endearing.

'If you say so, old thing,' I tartly mocked, and all at once asked myself what might be her reaction to his two shatteringly handsome sons! It just didn't bear thinking about!

What a strange and peculiar year that one turned out to be! The days and weeks seemed to draw themselves out, tight and anxious as an unquiet mind. The air itself became, with ever-increasing painfulness, unsettled and neurotic. For the first time in my life I got a boil on the back of my neck.

In November I was to compete for a scholarship to the Royal Academy of Music and my bowels were frequently in an uproar at the very thought of it.

I became excruciatingly aware of our little garden's charm. Never before had I observed its seasonal development in such an agonized state of anticipation — as though it might be for the last time. It came upon me with especial poignance at breakfast time, when we sat around the kitchen table, a marvellous sun-fuzzle quivering in the enormous fuchsia outside, the lilacs embalming the breeze in intoxicating rivalry with may-blossom, and a cuckoo shouting away somewhere in Councillor Norkett's garden. Pa's roses were wonderful that year, almost as fine as the thousand-trumpeted Begonia Grandiflora. When it rained at night I went into my brother Victor's room and we listened to the first quiet, slow patterings of rain on the leaves until, quite suddenly, the skies seemed to open, and we caught the strange scent of the scarlet blossoms.

That year, too, there was wheat in the Lovely Fields, and little did I suppose it was to be their last crop; that the building-boom was knocking at the door. The sleepy, quivering air was heavy with the smell of cow-mumble and crushed juices of succulent field-flowers. There seemed more bees about than usual. We had a swarm in our prodigally-fruiting greengage tree. When the bee-keeper moved it, that was the end. The remaining fruit withered away and the tree degenerated into a grudging, dry hag. It was an omen.

One evening the Gershom-Parkington quintette played *The Last Spring* by Edward Grieg on the wireless. For two days I gloomed around with nervous dyspepsia, my heart a dead weight on my chest.

C.T.Chamberlain, by now so high-coloured as to suggest a state of anti-mortem embalment, spoke of his joint-partnership between Pa and his arch-enemy, Mr Shigsby, who managed the gentlemens' department down in the bay-rummy humidity below.

What was Pa to do? Shigsby feared him and his tongue like the plague. When bad blood arose between them, as it all too frequently did, poor Shigsby went around with vivid pimples breaking out around his mouth like fairy-lights. On the other hand, Pa liked a quietly convivial life. Stress was anathema to him. Without the unruffled, silky calm of C.T. Chamberlain's presence about the place, Pa foresaw appalling ructions, especially when paper-work came into the picture. Pa detested clerical work, while Shigsby revelled in the prospect of pens and ledgers.

July came with the news that C.T. planned to retire for certain the following spring. Pa had until Christmas to make up his mind. I came, without clear reason, except perhaps the sense of insecurity they engendered, to abominate the sweet essences pouring from Chamberlain's door. The click of marcelling irons, singeing paper and warm oil agitated me, filled me full of craven terrors. I felt resentment towards poor old C.T. Surely the fellow was working off a long-standing grudge against Pa and his indispensability.

In the mean-time, confident in his talents and personality, Pa maintained a Micawber-like faith in something turning up, and sought counsel of the Sybil who dwells at the bottom of an empty glass.

I tried the same dodge one evening at the Swan Hotel in Lower High Street, and was as sick as a toad.

15

By Punt By Skindles

One glorious Saturday afternoon of that same July, with the heavy aroma of privet in the hedges hinting that summer days were drawing on a bit, and opulent petunias and gloxinias flaunting themselves in river-side gardens, I took Mooghie punting from Wilders down to Bray. She was superb in a sleeveless cotton dress of yellow and chocolate stripes, and white court shoes of woven bast. Her slight plumpness was now Junoesque and heroic. Her body had acquired the trained, taut yet fluid quality of the ballet girl, her back hollow and straight as a young fir-tree, her limbs seemingly governed by a law absolutely forbidding the slightest yielding to rigidity. To my prejudiced eye she put the very swans to shame.

There was a *Thé Dansant* at Skindles. The band was playing *Blue Skies*. That summer popular music was, like

There was a Thé Dansant at Skindles . . . waiters moved nimbly around the tables on the lawns in 1922.

Piccasso, going through a blue period: *Blue Moon, The Birth of the Blues, So Blue* . . . a vintage year. The couples swayed within open French doors, waiters moved nimbly around tables on the lawns, sharply tinkling tea-spoons punctuated a distant smother of chatter, occasionally and temporarily interrupted by a loud, male whisky-laugh like a mortar-bomb exploding.

'Do you fancy it, Mooghie?'

'God, no, darling! Such a common gaff, don't you think? I saw Doris Brown out there on the lawn.' She lit a cigarette. 'We are going to the Hotel de Paris. Now that's the kind of place that deserves our dancing!'

'What! And me with scarcely the oof to pay for the punt? Come off it Mooghie!'

'Oh, darling, don't get so agitated. Daddy has booked us a table on the telephone. Please don't be stuffy about it. I do so love dancing with you.'

'Your father!'

'Of course, Hubert. What a ridiculous creature you can be at times! Have you really been kidding yourself into believing he dosen't know about us? Mum's a bit annoyed with you for turning down our invitations, but it simply makes daddy grin. He asks me what kind of a bashful booby I go round the town swinging hands with. Mary Burn has given you rave-notices and half his female patients receive your father's ministrations. He knows you like the back of his hand, my love.'

She threw her cigarette away, turned to look after it.

'Oo-er! What WOULD Lord Desborough say?'

'But to let him pay for my teaing and dancing . . . What a rotten scrounging little worm he must think me!'

'You seem to forget that he's paying for my teaing and dancing too. You'll be calling yourself a lounge-lizard next. You're so over-scrupulous, Hubert!'

We fell in sudden shadow, gliding under Brunel's great arch. Mooghie knelt up on the cushions, pouting lasciviously.

'I love you preposterously,' she whispered.

'Uv you — osper — per — pos — sss' said the echo.

'You're a totally fascinating creature,' I said. 'Ma fille aux cheveux de lin!'

Skindle's Lawn, any Sunday in the Summer

BOATING   FISHING

"SKINDLES"

The Premier Sporting Hotel on the Thames

ESTABLISHED TWO CENTURIES

HUNTING   GOLF

PRIVATE LAWNS   ::   LANDING STAGE

AMERICAN BAR

LUXURIOUS LOUNGE FACING RIVER

OPEN AIR RESTAURANT   HARD COURT TENNIS

J. D. HODGSON, *Proprietor*.

Telephones :— 268 and 269.   *Telegrams :—*" Skindles, Maidenhead."
Railway Stations : Taplow and Maidenhead.

*Nothing much had changed by 1929 — there was still tea on
the lawn — and nimble waiters.*

155

'I really think we ought to stop first at the Island at Bray, don't you. Dancing will keep for half an hour, won't it?'

'Alright - not half!' my stomach gave a little heave. It was extraordinary how, with so much love between us there could subsist such intense shyness. Her dress was tied at each shoulder with a neat chocolate-coloured bow. My viscera performed another loop. We had made certain strides since that pathetic afternoon at the Cinema. And those nobles and nabobs over there at Gaiety Row: did they feel so, eagerly watching the Terpsichorean capers of their charmers from stage boxes at the 'Gaiety, Tiv' and Pav'?

I dug in my pole. I knew just the place. A little canal where water-rats swam, a hundred yards or so beyond the Hotel de Paris. Somebody waved from one of the little gravel beaches between towering willow-herb and loose-strife, a female very closely accompanied by a flashy gent in a wide, flat cap. She was far gone in pregnancy and I didn't exactly savour her enthusiastic greeting.

'Who on earth is that?' exclaimed Mooghie with some indignation.

'Her name is Mary-Anne Colyer,' I told her. 'Better known as The White Man's Burden.'

'Gracious!' observed Mooghie sympathetically. 'She looks more as if some white man had burdened her. Poor girl. She's thrown her whole life away!'

'It's her fifth,' I said. 'As my uncle's old cowman down in Norfolk might say: "She lurv ut — she ca-ant git enurf of ut!"'

Mooghie gave one of her ringing laughs. 'The Colonels Lady and Lilly O' Grady are sisters under the skin!' she warbled. 'Who is one to cast a stone?'

The Hotel de Paris hove in sight, but its Island called with the voice of Aphrodite. Hotly smelt the ripening corn in the afternoon sun, sickly-sweet the river-weed and river-mud, and short, thick willows leaned. Short of the Lock, I drove the punt hissing into the reeds.

Short of the Lock, I drove the punt hissing into the reeds.

That sense of unduly hastening time followed me to Cox Green Flower Show. Even the shattering glitter of the roundabout, all mirrors and gilt marquises, spasmodically striking tambourines and triangles, with its perpendicular thread of smoke going steadily skyward from the central chimney, and its enormously aggressive tonic and dominant shaking the air, so that you felt it in your entrails half a mile away, failed to shift that elegiac weight from my breast: that uncanny sense of seeing it all for the last time.

Mooghie had been forbidden to accept my invitation to the Show. The Doctor had at last taken umbrage at me. If I was too grand to take tea out at Mariposa, then his daughter was far too good to jostle and rub shoulders with a crowd of country chaw-bacons out at Cox Green. The time had come to chance my arm out at Cygnet Green.

In the meantime we went on meeting. Her parents, their irritation with me notwithstanding, trusted me as her companion. Why wouldn't they indeed? Mooghie had prattled of my virtues from the age of eight. They were too sensible to let that go for nothing.

But, as I made my way from stall to stall, from hot to hotter marquee, the more brightly and fragrantly things presented themselves to me, the sadder I got, the deeper grew my depression. Wonderful sword-length beans, fat peas, meticulously scrubbed and presented potatoes, tomatoes big as babies with their blandly pungent scent, roses enormously fragrant, many-shaded phloxes, musky and evocative of every midsummer afternoon festivity across the fecund breast of England; chiffon sweet peas, most feminine of all blooms . . . I could have sat down upon the trodden grass and wept my eye out!

I decided to be off, dodged all my friends and passed out through the gate at the far end of the field near the railway. The egregious tonic and dominant pumping of the roundabout followed in my wake until, beyond the dirty little brick railway arch at the bottom of Boyn Hill, I lost it at last. What was the rest of the afternoon and evening with its dancing and fireworks without Mooghie? Only her presence relieved me of this sickly atmosphere of tension.

16

Stuchberry & Fitzgibbon

A time came when I was obliged to soldier on without her. Aunt Laura returned from the Levant and, before we could say 'knife,' whisked her off to Blackpool where, at the North Pier Pavilion, Mooghie was to act as a replacement with a troup of girls in the summer show. It was experience, Laura said, starting at the bottom as all real performers should: rehearsing routines, sewing on sequins, maintaining costumes - on top of the two hours' daily practice on her guitar, and no favours as the niece of an important agent.

It came as no surprise to me. I had been expecting something of the sort. She was removed, I suspected, from my sphere of influence; they were trusting in a change of scene to bring about a change of heart. I might have reacted in the manner of a thwarted lad: have quarrelled melodramatically, issued ultimatums; made the lives of both a misery. I should have been so wrong.

We were not the Heavenly Twins for nothing. One glance at her face showed me my own wretchedness as in a mirror. Our facial resemblance sprang out as never before. Only that we loved each other so dearly stood at one moment between our parents and an unpleasant eventual shock.

When she had gone; when my clumsy old Ingersoll showed me five minutes past eight; I listened hard for her train leaving Maidenhead Station according to a weird eccentricity of time-tableing. Alas, the wind was wrong. All that hit my tympanum was the distant metallic drumming of a shunting line of trucks and the faint shrilling of a whistle.

I had made a dourly sardonic resolution. I was to write her a letter each morning, putting my whole soul into it, squeezing every drop of worship out as I have seen old ladies do in taking the wafer and the wine and then to forget her for the rest of the day — or at least try to.

The school holidays had begun, and that was cause for gratitude. I renounced my promises of hard work. Two hours at the piano should suffice, and the rest of the day I would call my own, dedicating it to wanton time-killing and idling. Thus I'd save my sanity.

I had made new friends. There was Cecil Hewitt from Bath Road whose father was a Saville Row tailor and very well-off. Cecil was one of the best-looking chaps I ever met. He got his father to make me a lovely light grey suit very cheaply, and together we created quite a dash. I got into the habit of going with him to tea dances at the Central Cinema at Reading, where we sometimes picked up most un-Mooghie-like girls and took them for rides in the car, which he borrowed from his rather over-indulgent Pa. Naturally I failed to mention these sometimes sleazy adventures in my letters to Blackpool.

Then there was the Swan Hotel and the Wrattles. Ma and Pa Wrattle were exactly like a cartoon by Phil May, she ample-skirted, sporting a bun in the centre of a head of bleached-blonde buffed-up hair, plump and sunny of face; Pa smart, doggish and elegant in fine tweeds, and with a face so richly scarlet with grog-blossoms you could scarcely tell, when he wore his red waistcoat, where it finished and his face began. Their attractive daughter, Marjory, had just become an apprentice at old C.T.'s. The two flax-blonde brothers, bronzed and wavy-haired, were great rowing-men, and it was a sight to see these handsome giants and their sister together in a punt. Such style they had.

I used to go there to play pontoon. Six or seven of us would squat around an enormous divan in the lounge upstairs with the sign-board squeaking outside. The Swan almost faced the Town Hall and the lounge actually did overlook the front of Upson's the chemist. One afternoon, as I was pondering whether to stick or twist, I chanced to look up from my cards and, in the window opposite, whom should I perceive but Dorothy Upson powdering her face in her camisole. Quel frisson!

It was, however, my loner's path that I chiefly followed in my idlings. By myself I attended All Saints one Sunday morning, intending to take the Sacrament. It was my first attendance for well over three years. As soon as he stopped socking my head for misdemeanours, Pa gave me freedom of choice in the matter of churchgoing. From then on, he told me, it was between myself and the black-beetles.

Nothing much altered. The Altwood kids Victor and I had formerly leered and ogled were now fine and disdainful creatures with busts. But there, other change was imminent. The School was about to move from Tittle Row down to Linton House at the top of Castle Hill.

But Mr Stuchberry was quite unchanged. No less massive in his surplice at the head of the choir, his huge bass voice resembling one of the lower-register organ-pipes gone peripatetic, he actually, turning in procession, concealed the rest for one brief moment, so that the sum total of their anthem seemed to proceed from the interior of his massive trunk. Mr Stuchberry was always the king-pin of the entire set-up for me. His half-spectacles, over which he peered with grim benevolence, his double, firm-fleshed chin, so beautifully shaven, the enormous solemnity of his demeanour . . . his stately presence made small potatoes of the incumbent, the Reverend Mahoney, with his blue Irish chin, patent leather hair and Byzantine posturings. Mrs Thorne and Miss Nichols, each side of the aisle, were heraldic supporting beasts in gigantic hats with drooping veils. Miss Jacobs, as usual, overcome by the fumes from the doomed Mr Ashley's thurible, was transported, a limp bundle, into the churchyard to recover.

Finally I decided not to communicate. The old ladies put me off with their spotted purple lips and the fact the Reverend Mahoney didn't appear to be making use of a napkin between sips.

Strolling home between Renee and Julie it struck me for the first time how heavy the motor-traffic was getting along the Bath Road, how some of the makes had a notably old-fashioned air. An Arrol-Johnson, for example, compared with a passing Lagonda, looked as ripe for extinction as formerly a Dodo mmight have done upon the Isle of Mauritius. At that very moment at the pavement's edge, I had such a vision of Mooghie kneeling in the punt kissing the air at me that my head swam.

Another of my stupid but agreeably time-consuming ploys was the mental collection of the truly fantastic plant-pots, seen in front parlour windows of the side streets of the district surrounding my home. I entertained a scatty notion of organizing a strolling club: La Societé des Amateurs des Potiches, perhaps. Powney, Portlock and Pennystone Road I travelled, three adjoining thoroughfares, so named by Victorians after a former High Steward of the Town and Verdurer of Windsor Great Park. The yield here was rich and plentiful. Brass, china, copper, earthenware, tin and bronze: wrought, twisted, cast and moulded. In Portlock Road I discovered an almost life-sized Alsatian dog in terra cotta with rock-roses sprouting from a row of holes down its spine. That was a dilly: almost as bizarre as the buxom ballet dancer in plaster in Belmont Road, pirouetting in a bosky welter of pelargoneums. In Forlease Road a marble mosque took my breath away. Four houris suspended eight richly tinted breasts from a gilded lattice and beneath, four dumpy Levantine babies stretched in vain tearfulness after the maternal goodies. A wag had appended a card whereon was printed the words: What flavour, duckies? In Keble Road I drew a blank. Very posh down one side it was, with front gardens discreetly beshrubbed. On the opposite side — where I recalled nice homely old allotments with delapidated little sheds and gently steaming muck-moulds — less genteel, not to say jerry-built houses, took their tone from across the road.

One drizzly afternoon in Chummy's Row, where the cottage fronts abutted on the pavement, I espied a beautiful china swan such as one used to see in dairy-shops, with white and brown eggs looking deliciously appetizing between half-spread wings. It had been under my inspection some few minutes,

How heavy the motor-traffic was getting along the Bath Road . . . an Arrol-Johnson looked ripe for extinction. As a kid I had seen an aeroplane settle in the corn. Now Donald Stevenson offered all manner of modern motors — and de Havilland aeroplanes, if you could afford one.

163

before my absently focussing eyes, taking in the contents of the room behind, beheld an elderly and singularly ill-favoured old gentleman squatting stark naked upon a chamber-pot. Quite unoffended he saluted me with a toothless grimace and a beckoned invitation to enter his hovel. That was the end of La Societé des Amateurs des Potiches.

Mooghie was having a bad time of it. She detested Blackpool and the head girl was a bitch. Endless rehearsals on top of two hours' daily guitar-practice were killing her, on top of which sewing and general maintenance of her costumes were roughening her finger-tips, ruining her touch. Everthing was unfair and hateful and mum, coerced by Aunt Laura, was being no help at all. A stage-hand had pinched her bottom and nothing — not a damned thing — had been done about it. Show business was Hell!

I wrote her reams of sympathy and tenderness, simultaneously unable to resist feelings of rather spiteful exultation at the knowledge that life was not a bed of roses apart from me.

I met an elderly dragon at a concert given by Mark Hambourg, Called Mrs Fitzgibbon, who invited me to tea at her house in Laburnam Road. I never really got to know her cats because there were so many of them. Daphnis and Cloë, I recall because of their incontinence. The old lady had what she called pregnancy boxes all over the shop, and every other ten minutes or so there occurred a sharp discharge of what sounded like toy-soldiers' musketry, followed by the appalling stench of feline excrement. After a consequently rather queasy tea she prevailed upon me to play to her upon a wonderful Bechstein. Terrified, I acceded, performing for her a group of Rachmaninov transcriptions over which she went into ecstasies. She was, I think, a tiny bit mad, and addressed me thenceforward, entirely without irony, as 'cher maitre.' But I grew to like her and to enjoy her conversation, for she was a very civilized person, had travelled widely and possessed a fantastical gift for describing her many adventures — some of which might even have been described as aristocratically seamy! She had great generosity, and gave me, not only a heap of extraordinarily useful music, but also a pile of French paperback novels, illicit acquisitions of her girlhood in India, by Gyp, Pierre Loti and Guy de Maupassant.

She lent me a copy of *Dracula* by Bram Stoker and for me the Court House Road end of the Avenue was never quite the same again. With fields beyond, it mightn't have been so bad, but recent building had got well ahead and the scene was depressingly urbanized. The great field where, as a cream-puffy kid in buster-suit, I had seen an aeroplane settle like a frail insect in the corn, was now a nasty mélange of completed houses with rudimentary gardens, half-built ones cluttered up with ugly rubble, and skeletal beginnings, all ropes, lime-stained planks and wooden scaffold-poles anchored in barrels of earth. Unfamiliar and raucous children invaded the Avenue, regarding the chestnut trees with appraising eyes.

I was not alone in my Draculian trauma. The horrible story became very fashionable and many were the lone afficionados to be seen passing up or down the middle of the Avenue after dusk, bending quick frightened glances from one line of trees to the other.

It was not the appalling Count who so agitated my viscera, though he was bad enough, Heaven knows, but Lucy his first victim among the protagonists. Of course I had to locate her tomb amid the yews and laurels surrounding the rather ghastly Chapel, high-walled and containing two sheltered rows of seats, upon whose white backs tormented loiterers scratched complicated and detailed graffiti.

Nosferatu, the undead, I saw against my shrinking retina; her fearful wraith and fanged snarl, a stolen baby in her arms, gliding in the Cemetery ways, hell bent for her bed of blood-rank soil. The owls whose voices had sounded so deliciously eerie and gothic, now threatened to take on a new and sinister character. But that I would not have. Owls were beautiful: swift smooth haunters of the night, perchers upon farm-gate-posts. There had been a time when I sought their pellets with palpitating curiosity. They were also the birds of

Athena, my favourite Greek deity. So, with a sense of leather-winged little demons infesting the night, I opened the sash of my window at the bottom one night and sat upon the sill, with my feet on the wash-house roof and dared the Nosferatu to do their worst! The owls should stay on the side of the angels. But I kept a firm grip upon my clove of garlic!

By and by the horror of the Bloofer-Lady diminished, dispelled by moonlight visions of Mooghie with her inimitable chic and grace. Weeks elapsed, however, before I discarded my clove of garlic.

So, what with pontoon at the Swan, and tea-dancing with Cecil at Reading, pot-collecting in the high-ways and bye-ways, swimming at the baths at the bottom of East Street with Renee and Co, and taking tea with Mrs Fitzgibbon and her cats, I found, one morning, that five weeks had doddled their way into the past, and that in my hand was a telegram from Mooghie to say she would be back home sometime within the next two days. I learned later how twice she had worked herself up into a royal rage, and had only been deterred from packing a few clothes and storming home by Aunt Laura's vow to wash her hands of her for good and all.

Thus it came about that, on the following afternoon, killing time like mad, measuring out my hours with cigarettes, staggering around in a state of stifling excitement, I bought myself a seat in the ninepennies at Bridge Street Pictures, to see *Metropolis* and, as I blinked my way like a mole into the sun-light, there she was, and where she had been a beautiful girl before, now she was a splendidly lovely young woman, taller in her stiletto heels, golden in her Chinese sam cheong and far, far too good for me. My ascendancy, I felt, was over. I really had to grow right up to merit her. The rather arrogant, Greek-style beauty of her mother told me that I had better do just that.

17

The Heavenly Twins

I sat at the end of Claremont Pier with the anglers. A genuine East Anglian sky exploded above in bursts of bounding cloud in every shape and shade of grey and purple, interspersed with tenuously edged patches of bright blue. With the sun shining, one's very marrow rejoiced, but its withdrawal behind one of those gushes of aerial ebbulience put the crushers on high spirits. Manic-depressive weather, it was. Waves slurped and sucked at the piles below. At the horizon, three coasting steamers dragged their skeins of smoke, and from up the beach the goatish, brazen, ramishly indecent voice of Mr Punch shrieked: 'That's the way to do it! — That's the way to do it!'

It was Thursday: the parents due back in the afternoon, grandma refractory and no letter from Mooghie by the morning post. I sighed despite Mrs Grintforth's assurance of the frequent arrival of the morning post at mid-day. Now the tiniest irregularity in my rapport with my 'twin' filled me with grave, almost superstitious misgivings. So much promise of a bright and hopeful future and I must be absent from her, unable to protect her in case of harm threatening her. What harm? It was absurd. Yet my mind was assailed by torturing anxiety. Pure neurosis maybe. It had been at me since the moment I got to this dull and boring place. That rain-storm had started it off. In spite of the sunshine and the freshness of the breeze off the white-horsed sea, a cloud seemed to hang over everything. Everything wobbled precariously.

Way up the beach, a halma-piece in the distance, Grandma reclined in a beach-chair, read her Marie Corelli and, I presumed, sucked juicily the liquorice torpedos she had purchased that morning. My brothers were squandering my last five bob at the Fun Palace just up the pier.

167

Why had I declined to follow Doctor Campbell's advice and simply refused to come on this stupid holiday? I closed my eyes. The sea-gulls swept by like shadows across the lighter darkness of closed lids, their exacerbating cries a piercing assault upon jangled nerves.

Again I sat on the verandah steps of Mariposa: spacious, sweet with the vines of jasmine and honeysuckle and the Doctor's cigar. Mooghie was unpacking the last of the things the station waggon had delivered that afternoon, and what she was unpacking had an alien, disturbing effect upon my spirits, the same sort of effect as afflicted me at sight of the Water Tower as seen from the foot-bridge over the Wycombe line between College Road and the Crescent. Grey-blue brick it was, with a cubic bulge at the top, sliced out with crenellations like an Italian tower of the middle ages, but with a morbid-looking row of leaden false windows, like a mourning clown's waistcoat-buttons. It reared itself aggressively above the tree-tops, unfamiliar and hostile.

Two pairs of tap-shoes she unpacked, a pair of slim, black, patent-leather shoes with very sexy high heels, and two pairs of ballet shoes. Then came a lovely gilt fan, a pair of castanets and an enormous Spanish comb. Finally she shook out a scarlet, scented, silk shawl with a golden fringe, went in and draped it across the tail of the piano.

I grew yet more dispirited. A few weeks had done all this. She was unmistakeably of the theatre now, talking its rakishly sophisticated language, quoting *The Stage* and *The Performer* like a regular trouper, and expressing, in the way she wore her clothes and used her voice, the spirit of a dressing-room shared for weeks with laughing, back-biting, wise, disdainful high-spirited girls, with digs, the tea-leaves down the lavatory and fags drawn on in hasty puffs in intervals of making up. How could I, a confirmed ninny and stay-at-home, ever hope to share in such a life. Yet that was what was being planned for me. I had a feeling of being coerced and driven like one of my uncle's Norfolk bullocks. She had opened another case, and produced a series of gowns that might have tempted the finger and thumb of the most blameless of young stage-hands. With a side-ways and very wry smile I wondered what Canon Drummond would have thought about it all.

'Why the Lumie Tree?' I asked her. 'Pseudo Acacia is good enough, surely. It's even more suitable for such a gorgeous-looking tree.'

The garden at Mariposa stretched out before us, the Lumie Tree across the mere, the house beyond.

She straightened herself, drawing her azure house-gown with seductive leisureliness over her bare shoulders.

'Look when it lightens again,' she told me — 'there, now — look!'

As if a giant phosphorescent hand had flattened itself upon several miles of dark distance, the trees and barns of Burnham and its Church flared into a weirdly wavering glare. The clouds weaved, flickered and seemed on the verge of dancing like a gargantuan will-o'-the-wisp.

But the Lumie Tree!....It took fire like a plumed torch, its flames flashing yet livid, vivid yet at the same time lugubrious. I had never seen a specimen of its size. It must have been full forty feet in height and, at the richest season of its foliage, brought to my fancy the funeral-pall of the Inca Emperor, Atahualpa, done to death by Spanish Pizzaro, the Conquistador, for his golden wealth. The tree disappeared and we were in velvety blackness once more.

'Don't you see, darling? In the dawn and the twilight it's luminous. It gives out light when there's hardly light at all in the atmosphere. Like as if it's stored up all the light of the previous day in its leaves. We call it the Lumie-Tree for short. Perhaps you find that a tiny bit soppy. Family manners and customs so often seem so to outsiders.'

'Of course I don't. I think Lumie Tree is charming. But how on earth old is it to have reached such a size?'

'Daddy planted it the day I was born. He's been terrified of something happening to it — or me — ever since.'

'You mean he's identified you and your fate with a damn' tree? Him, an ex-Guards officer and a doctor to boot? How do you and your mum feel about such a bit of silliness?'

'Oh, mum's as superstitious as he is. She just doesn't let on. You know the way thunder-storms sometimes move up and down the Valley all day without seeming able to get out....? Well, daddy's on the jump all the time till they clear away. Sometimes at weak moments it's not all that funny knowing a damn' tree may be a matter of life or death to one.'

'But it's sheer and utter bloody nonsense,' I exclaimed angrily. 'You forget it, Mooghie. Damn the tree! Remember you're alright with me. Always have been, always will be. Don't you let them make a doomed Hamadryad out of you, my little love!'

'A Hamadryad! What a lovely idea! Morbid but lovely!'

Another flash of sheet-lightning revealed the classical ripeness of her lips, parted for kissing. Crickets clinked their tiny chains and the reeds of the mere stirred startlingly. A moorhen squawked. From the garden way behind us faintly drifted the scents of stocks and tobacco-plants. Together we giggled and chanted: 'Isn't it all lovely?'

'Mooghie,' I said. 'Has this evening been real?'

'How do you mean, darling - real?'

'Well, your parents being so nice to me and all that?'

'My dear, why shouldn't they be nice to you. They don't entertain a genius every week-end.'

'Really, Mooghie, a genius! You mustn't laugh at my tiny talent.'

'No, neither must you fish for compliments — at least not with me. You know very well how good you are. All the kids told me but I never expected anything like you gave us tonight. Not only the Lizst trancendental studies and the lovely Debussy, but the way you played my Rachmaninov accompaniments. Do you know, you're the best accompanist I've ever heard. No, I mean it.'

'But does your Aunt Laura mean it all — about going to the Varconi School with you and the double act?'

Mooghie laughed. 'Darling, she can't wait to get her hands on you. She means every word of what she promised. She'll send us right to the top, the pair of us! You'll see.'

'I'm going to be scared stiff all the time. How am I going to face bookings at private parties? I've never played in public in

170

my life. I never supposed for a moment that she'd be getting me off so soon. Booking me solid, as she puts it, until we've got our act together.'

'You wait until you've learned the fundamentals and there won't be any holding you. There's only getting on stage, taking a bow, getting off, then taking a call. Nothing, my pet, that you won't be doing on your head in a couple of weeks.'

'What I can NOT understand is the way your father seems to like me. I'd have expected him to take a dim view of my sort. What have two chaps like us in common?'

'Oh, come on, Hubert. Don't, for the love of Mike, be so self-deprecating. Do you think he'd have virtually invited you to live with us if he didn't think a lot of you? I just can't wait until you come back to settle into the studio over the garage. Do you really think your father will move away to Norwich?'

'I've got a nasty feeling that he will. He thinks everything is going to go right for him. He's a real Micawber, you see!'

'Perhaps you're looking on the gloomy side, sweetie. Perhaps he'll decide to stay at Chamberlain's. Why, he's got everything there. All the popularity. Women rave about him. I've heard them.'

She gasped theatrically and slipped off the top of her gown. 'Gracious, it's getting hotter all the time. Darling, do take off your shirt and let's get carnally connected — just for a minute; just the top of us — until the lightning comes again!'

'Alright, but that's the lot, Mooghie. Remember we're the Heavenly Twins!'

Across the mere, away beyond the Lumie Tree, the lights of Mariposa twinkled: the verandah's more brightly than the rest. By lamplight, regardless of moths and leatherjackets, Barbara, Aunt Laura and the Doctor were playing whist with a stiff, overly-pukka chap called Tim Hewson from Marlow Road, who was also stopping overnight.

The lightning played once more. By its flare I drank up her beauty, dived deep into those magnificent, oblique eyes. The Lumie Tree was waving slightly its plumes of gold. I realized that I really didn't care much for that tree.

We were in the dark again. Mooghie buttoned up her gown and I my shirt. 'There,' I told her. 'Thank your lucky stars you're still *virgo intacta* and we'll not be riddled with anxiety all the time I'm away at mucky Lowestoft. And now explain to me the real secret of my success with your parents.'

'So very simple, my pet. You remember how frail I was when I first came to Queen Anne? — The frosty morning when that robin sang in our faces and the lovely red apples shone in the sun?'

'As if it was yesterday. You and your scented beads and your dear little gingham drawers!'

'Well, I'd always been an ailing brat and all at once I wasn't ailing any more. I fell in love with you so dearly that instead of dreading school I came to long for it. Mum and Daddy were jubilant - I being their only chick, you see. They interviewed Miss Mayne one morning and she showed us to them in the playroom, just at a moment when you were making me laugh my head off. They seemed to see in you a psychic talisman between me and all evil and wickedness. I felt health and energy pouring into me whenever you held my scented beads and smelt them. Like a sort of wonderful magic, all that marvellous, marvellous energy of yours! I lived on you like a vampire!'

'Not a vampire, please....anything but that!'

I took out my cigarettes. At that moment the Doctor's voice could be heard calling: 'Mooghie, where have you got to, m'dear?'

We got up. 'We're here, daddy,' she called out in her newly resonant stage voice. 'We're watching the lightning in the Lumie Tree. Such Heaven. We're coming now. The lightning seems about over and the midges are biting like cannibals!'

'Then hurry up before you catch confounded malaria. It's supper-time. You hungry, Hubert?'

'A bit,' I said.

'Then get a move on, unless you want cold waffles for supper.'

He returned to the verandah, whistling *Charmaine*.

'Don't light your cigarette yet,' said Mooghie. 'Wait until we're nearly there, then we'll make our entrance, smoking with an air *bien degagé* and *comme il faut*, like Noël Coward characters — and Hubert, darling, I'm so very glad to be *virgo intacta*. You really are a bit of a dear, you know.'

With a flourish of her fog-horn, the *Marchioness of Breadelbane* swished by the pier-head, exhibiting like a gallery of Hogarthian portraits her pleasure-bent passengers. They presented an appearance of dream-like surrealism, all gazing shoreward: the schematic look of a vast mural painting from the brushes of massed but well-organised children.

The anglers cursed the great swishing paddle-wheels, when one of them was suddenly straining to land a most enormous conger-eel. Several fellow-anglers hastened to aid him with his dangerous catch. I got up and set off to fetch Grandma home to lunch. Several men had got their knives out and I began to feel sorry for that conger. From my pocket I drew Mooghie's scented beads: almost, alas, bereft by the years of perfume, but soaked with the very essence of her personality like a little girl's love-lavished doll. I felt, I think, something of what my Catholic Granny at Reading did, fingering her Rosary amidst the bustling traffic of Southampton Road or Friar Street.

There was nothing from Mooghie. Now, a confirmed worrier, I felt a gnawing at my vitals. Not a day had she missed of all the five weeks at Blackpool. What could be wrong? The smell of Ma Grintforth's beef stew should have been delicious after a morning's blow on the pier. Instead, it hit my gastric membranes like a spray of vitriol. I felt as sick as a toad. When Grandma got mean and querulous with the boys I gave her what policemen call a good rollicking, upbraiding her for her secrecy over the parents' absence in Norwich, telling her flat that I knew damned well what was going on and, not at all politely, what I thought of her generally. Perturbation lent an edge to my anger. The old besom started to pipe her eye. Pitiless, recalling past severities, I tried to borrow telephone money from her but, of course, without avail. Her refusal drove me almost to desperation. If only I had not lashed out on

Victor's new slacks and all those blow-outs at the Cosmo Café....If just then Grandma had bidden me neither a borrower nor a lender be — umph! I would more than probably have knocked off the beaver hat and danced a dance of fiendish malice upon it.

Practical old Victor said: 'Wait for the evening post. If nothing turns up for you then I'll rifle her bloody old hand-bag. It's my fault. If you hadn't bought me these trousers....'

'Nuts!' I said. 'I'd have squandered it on something else.'

All at once a taxi drew up at the door, crammed with Norfolk relatives. Like a jack-in-the-box, his eyes out on stalks, Pa shot out, streaked up the front path, tumbled through the front door and grabbed me by the arm.

'Out!' he hissed. 'Out through the back-way. I've had all I can put up with for a day or two! I must talk to you or bust!'

To the amazed Ma Grintforth he raised a thin, theatrical and warning finger. 'Steady!' jerked out Pa. 'Stand by to repel boarders!'

We left her with her ellipitcal mouth turned to the Euclidian circle and were instantly galloping through a mysteriously cluttered hinterland of dust-bins, tool-sheds, flag-staffs, shrimping-nets and convolvulus-smothered shrubs and fruit bushes; neither did we stop until we stood panting at the Lighthouse saloon-bar.

'A double whisky, Jimmy,' he gasped. 'And — a — half of bitter for — me boy!'

We were served. The taxi passed on its way back to the Station Rank. After a shortish interval there swept by the hastening pageantry of ma's kinfolk. Herself, Aunts Edie, Jane and Trudy: Uncles Jack, Arthur and Bertie. All looked very angry, out of breath and out of step.

'They're all off to the Cosmo for lunch,' sneered Pa. 'It'll be a spartan one because I shan't be there to pay. I wonder if the parsimonious pip-squeaks will go dutch.' He gave a short laugh. 'That Bertie....there's no more than five stone of him yet he stuffs like a porker!'

If only I had not lashed out on Victor's new slacks . . . The brothers take their ease in the sunshine of yesteryear, Victor on the right.

175

His features suddenly collapsed into a mask of tragedy. At first I thought he would burst into tears. Instead he pushed his empty glass at the barman. 'Give us another, Jimmy, and have one yourself!' And to me: 'Well, me boy, God help me, I've done it!'

'Done it?' I mouthed stupidly. 'Done what — as if I didn't know already. You're shipping your poor damned family off to Norwich. That's it isn't it?'

He drank off his whisky in two gulps and stared into the bottom of the glass; but the Sybil was clearly not at home, because his eye, when it met mine, was vacant and deserted as an empty house.

'What on earth made you do it, Pa?' I asked him. 'You'd have done better to have made up your mind to put up with Shigsby surely. You could have trodden a worm like him under-foot.'

'I'm no good at it, my boy. I'm always sorry for 'em — worms. Fellow feeling, I suppose.' He gave himself a shake and ordered another whisky. He seemed in a state to booze without getting the slightest bit drunk. I'd seen him like it before. Suddenly his face would go as white as paper and he'd fall, stiff as a board, into anything that resembled in the slightest detail a bed.

'You know, Pa, I shan't be able to come with you.'

'What!' His face was suddenly bright red with rage.

'I'm going to live out at Cygnet Green with the Campbells. Muriel's aunt is an agent and she's interested in my work. It seems I could go places with her help. And what would there be for me in Norwich? I must stay around where my livelihood is likely to be. And they've offered me a nice flat.'

His anger drained away. He nodded slowly. 'Well, perhaps we're both going to get rich and respectable. These ghouls want to make a bloated capitalist of your old man. What do you think of that?'

'I think they'll worry you to death. Can't you change your mind, for God's sake?'

'Fraid not. All signed, sealed and delivered. I've taken a place in the middle of Norwich. In the middle of the Market

Place. In for a penny, in for a pound. Your Mother's all cock-a-hoop to get amongst her dear relations again. You can't really blame her, I suppose. Been living from hand to mouth for years. Wants a bit of prosperity. I've got no push, you see, need somebody to prod me along.'

'But you're going to miss all your old pals, aren't you?'

'I am that — and the old Windsor Castle and the Pond House and going up and down Castle Hill on me old green bicycle — and me roses.' He shook his head sadly, then: 'You are sure you can trust these Campbell people not to let you down? It's a bit of a step to take.'

'Don't you worry about me,' I said and saw Mrs Grintforth's youngest boy coming in with a orange envelope in his hand — a telegram. My heart turned over. It was for Pa. He said: 'Hello, Timmy, me boy. You oughtn't to be in here, you know.'

'F'you — s'urgent — Chap's waitin.' said Timmy laconically. Pa slit the envelope, glanced at the enclosed slip. Without a second's hesitation he whipped out his neat little note-book and pencil, tore out a leaf, scribbled a few words and put it into Timmy's hand.

'Tell him "coming at once" 'he snapped. 'And here's a bob for yourself. Now cut off quick!'

Well might Pa have assumed his condotterie's po-face. I knew something had befallen my girl. I had know it since this morning. It was I who was 'coming at once,' despite jellied legs and a slowly revolving bar-room. Pa handed me the telegram, then ordered a glass of brandy.

'Just a mouthful,' he said gently. 'Swizzle it around a bit before you swallow. You're not used to it but it'll do you good all the same.'

The telegram read: 'My daughter in accident stop calling for Hubert stop beg you let him come stop Campbell.'

We neurotics are resilient. The room and its contents resumed their customary fubsy banality. I got to my feet. My legs were stiff and aching but reasonably firm.

'Good lad,' commended Pa. 'Your colour's coming back. Look....You sit down in that chair while I go and pack the little leather case for you with your night-things. Shan't be a jiffy. Jimmy, pack him up a couple of ham sandwiches for the journey and look up the next train to London.'

He was gone, as usual, entirely forgetful of himself in another's crisis. I clasped the scented beads and fought to keep down the hideous images that assaulted my mind's eye. When Pa returned he found me wide-awake and resolute. If I got there with all speed Mooghie would be safe. Hadn't she always been alright with me.

'Look,' jerked out Pa, 'I've got five — six of the readies — '

'Pa,' I objected, 'It'll leave you broke!'

'Nonsense. Did you know about y'r mother's little hoard? She's been holding out on me, bedamned. Off we go — so long Jimmy!'

He knocked back what remained of the brandy. We made for the Station. He insisted on seeing me off. 'What's a Pa for, for God's sake?' he snapped.

I dared not answer him. It was toughness or tears. I chose the former. But, as his elegant, deceptively frail-looking shape was snatched from my vision by the curve in the line, I was thankful to have shaken his scarred hand and to have kissed him on the cheek in farewell. I hadn't done that for a year or two.

I was alone in the compartment until Beccles. I crouched dry-eyed in the corner, smoking the tortoiseshell Virginia Pa had bought me, trying to think of anything but Mooghie's accident, wondering how long we might expect to remain Maidonians: whether long enough to see the conkers break their cases and tumble from velvety pockets; whether long enough to sink our teeth into our crisp Blenheim apples, to bid all our friends farewell.

But I was not departing, was I? I had my flat at Cygnet Green to go to. I had a career before me and —

In a fit of dizzying despair I came with an appalling mental concussion against what I had been trying to avoid. Mooghie....Supposing anything were to happen to Mooghie. In cold-sweating brevity, what if her injuries had already proved fatal and I was destined to find her dead !

I wouldn't accept such a possibility at any price. But why had her father not given the cause of her mishap? A speeding car?....the level crossing just short of Cygnet Green?....the dangerous, brackened lip of Wilburn Quarry, where she sometimes walked her dog?....

I spent the time waiting at Norwich Station vainly trying to telephone her home. I tried three times and each time the line was engaged. A whistle blew, the engine answered. Aghast I seized rain-coat and case. A porter swore as I tumbled in and he slammed the door on my heels.

In Norfolk the harvest was in full swing. Reapers and binders clutched at the crops, bound them and tossed them out to the men and women, sunburned and sweating, who built them into shocks. Occasionally the smoke of a gun could be seen and a rabbit or a hare somersaulted and died in the teeth of greyhounds or fierce little terriers.

Diss must have been the land of clay-coloured clouds. You could have depended upon them as surely as wasps in plum-time. Last week's weather reversed itself. At Colchester the rain teemed down in sheets. I was by now just sourly tempered. A farrier's cold iron. It had to be thus. Sharp anxiety or sorrow driven to the limit and you might well open the carriage door and take the horrid plunge.

I taxied to Paddington through an appalling thunder-storm. I put on my raincoat and lit my last Tortoiseshell. In the pocket of the mac were Mooghie's remaining Abdullahs. Who said the old man wasn't thoughtful?

In the taxi I imagined I felt hungry. I began to snivel and nibble at one of the ham sandwiches, gagged and, remembering the appetite of London pigeons, chucked the food out of the taxi window.

At Paddington, a thirty minute wait. Again I tried to get Mariposa. The line seemed to be dead. At Hayes and Harling, mentally and physically exhausted, I went off into a dead sleep and had a short but eerie dream.

I dreamed I woke up in the carriage. The lights had gone dim and on the opposite seat crouched Monkey-Man, regarding me with a look of murder. I endeavoured to get to my feet but seemed to be held to the seat by a ton of lead. A dream....yes, but the lights of early evening were flashing past, and the train's rhythm was as clear and insistent as in the world of wakefulness. For what was like an age we stared at each other. How super-real some people are in one's dreams! His slanting flinty eyes and chimp's upper lip were as real as if searching the faces of Miss Burn's girls on Castle Hill. All at once he lurched forward and thrust his hideous features into my face.

'Moor-ell!' he croaked, 'Moor-ell!'

I awoke in a cold sweat. The train was running in to the station. In fancy's ear I heard that croaking voice.

'Maid'n'ead!' a porter was shouting. 'Maid'n'ead!'

I scrambled dizzily to my feet and clutched my things. With a furtive look back at the opposite seat, I tumbled with a wild look around me to the sodden, twilit platform. It was indeed Maidenhead. Now what? Impossible to retrace my way by rail. I remembered that I had money and somehow staggered down to the subway; same old fish and wet cardboard stink strengthened by foul weather. The streets reeked too as streets are apt to do after a downpour following a rainless month. Saturated back-yards, mildew, privet, concentrated dogs' urine.

The storm had passed on. But fagged and worried to death as I was this was still Maidenhead — my Maidenhead. Brunel's embankment shovelled out of Grenfell Park, the little offices and shops, a light in Mrs Timberlake's old flat and Ma's old tea-shop, now called Estelle's. On stiff legs I sought out Mr Rance and his taxi.

I found him after a short search in the Jug and Bottle of the Bell. At first he refused point-blank to go so far out in such weather. After another and closer look he asked me: 'You in some sort of trouble, son?'

'No: someone else is. You remember my girl-friend, Miss Campbell?'

'What 'er you used to 'ave yer tea with at yer Ma's old place?'

'Yes, Mr Rance. She's in a very bad way. I've come all the way from Lowestoft since dinner-time and I fell asleep and missed Taplow. Please, Mr Rance.'

Perhaps he remembered all Ma's flasks of tea. Perhaps Mooghie's eyes. At all events he swigged off his ale, gave a tug at his thick black moustache and, without a word, led me out under the Clock Tower and, pushing me into the back seat of his taxi, spread a rug to cover my now rather damp legs. Two cranks and his little cracker-box broke wind and joggled into life. In a cloud of blue smoke we swerved from Station Approach, crossed King Street and whined off into Queen Street.

Like bees, human-beings return to the hive, with the difference that, instead of pollen, it is impressions they carry at their bellies. My eyes consumed what we passed with a laboured concentration. The Railway Tavern kept by the eccentric Major Ford, Balsons the outfitters, sweet Sue Hunt's, Reeves's sweet shop, where the yellow ice-cream slipped out of the concavity in the thick glass dish if you didn't look out with your wafer, and where the ice-blocks gave you that strange little ache in the nape of your neck; the leather goods shop of pretty May Coddrington's father. A short glimpse to the right and there was Mr Wright, emerging from his cinema for a breath of fresh air. Across High Street, Spindlers was closed, but the Swan had a mildly convivial air.

Maidenhead was not quite Maidenhead as yet. Lowestoft was all mixed up with it, my fevered journey and the nightmare I had just woken from — not to speak of agonizing concern for what might be awaiting me at Mariposa.

From the Bridge the river wore its worst wet-weather looks. Willows dripped dejectedly; the fans of punts swung like coffins at the rafts; a few lights twinkled ineffectually in the half-light. There were even a few sordid fairy-lights over the lawn at Bridge House. And to think of the rhapsodical morning, less than a week ago, when I walked dreaming over the Bridge, remembering Mrs Melbury and her vicious hatred of the gentry, Gaiety Row and its ripe ladies. A fat lot of good

my ritual touching of the pillar had done. True, I had had my
victory over Big-Boy Baker. But what, after all, was that? In
exchange for Mooghie's safety he might, and welcome, have
socked hell out of me forever.

Outside Skindles two motors had collided and a rowdy
altercation was going on.

Soon we were through Taplow, and the scent of rain-soaked
meadows stole into the feazy little car, with others of sodden
pine-needles and stubble. It was now dark and Mr Rance's
lights poor and dim. Glancing through the tiny rear window I
was able to see the sky clearing, and a few stars hazily
glimmering.

Cygnet Green halt was deserted. Carefully Mr Rance guided
his little vehicle in and out of the few remaining lanes, drew up
at the gates of Mariposa and pushed aside the glass partition.

' 'Ere we are then,' he said. 'You won't mind if I don't go up
the drive. If I turns round this 'ere bit o' green, I c'n be on me
way quick-sticks. I hopes you finds yer young lady gowin' on
well. It'll be five and six for an ole pal, son — and me regards
to your Ma when you sees 'er.'

He ground away out of hearing. I turned through the gate
and saw the lights of the house, and, distantly, the light of
Cliveden. Something shone elfinly to my left and there came to
my ears a strangely loud rustling of leaves. It was the Lumie
Tree away by the mere. I realized once more that I just didn't
like the thing at all. It was like a beautiful, gloating devil in this
pleasant garden. Yet suddenly, while I was disliking it, there
came upon me the most exquisite sense of relaxation, a
soothing feeling of nonchalance, a most odd consciousness of
having emerged from a torture-chamber, untwisted and
unbroken.

I pulled at the iron bell-handle. The door was answered by
Netta, the parlour-maid, and behind her towered the Doctor.

In a moment I was in front of a blazing fire in the arms of
Mooghie's mum and being told that Mooghie was in no danger
after all.

18

The Lumie Tree

A group of strolling naturalists came upon Monkey-Man, whining his way through the woods, a stick bearing blood-stains in one hand and, entwined about the filthy fingers of the other, a thick tress of honey-blonde hair which three of the party recognized immediately. One of them fainted away on the spot.

He put up no resistance when the police came to take him away, just crouched in the moss like a trapped and abject beast keening 'Moor-ell — Moor-ell!' over and over again: clutching the golden tress to his grime-tapestried waistcoat.

A few yards away crouched the dog Tutu, whining, trembling and terrified, and a pace or two away, like a crumpled flower sunk in last year's wrinkled beech-leaves, Mooghie: blood in her hair, brutally beaten about the body and legs and her beautiful silk Chinese gown torn to tatters.

'Thank God,' said Barbara, 'there was no sign whatever of his having sexually assaulted her. He seems to have picked upon our daughter as a sort of scape-goat for all the other young girls who — and can one blame them — shunned him and to have worked off all his spite and spleen upon her.'

'The authorities should have listened to Mary Burn,' I said. 'Heaven knows she's complained to them often enough.'

'Well, dear boy, my husband will see that they put him away this time. Otherwise no child will be safe from him. Already they're talking about the Maidenhead Monster.'

She replenished my coffee cup. I could hear the deep voice of the Doctor from his study, wiring the news of my safe arrival to Pa before telephoning the Station Master at Taplow to pay off the driver, waiting for me since late afternoon.

'That telegram must have been a most terrible shock to you, my dear, and perhaps we should have held our horses awhile. But if you could have seen the condition she was in this morning, poor child - such a quiet, self-possessed little girl she always was — in a state of frightening hysteria . . . and then the damnable telephone ringing and ringing . . . her friends, the Press, the Police — even the most astonishing cranks! Darling, there was one sweet-sounding old gentleman I didn't know from Adam who, in the middle of his weepy commiserations, suddenly asked me in a tone like warm treacle if she had been raped, and begged for minute and intimate particulars. Can you imagine? I nearly fainted!'

She offered me a cigarette. Too angry for comment I puffed furiously. She went on: 'Then we got to blaming ourselves, of course. We have been so stupidly protective, you know. In Morocco she was perfectly safe and sound with Laura and at Blackpool she went through the entire season with nothing worse than a pinched bottom — and that was by a shrivelled little lad who was terrified to death by what he had done! Yet here, no more than a half mile from her own home, she is beaten half to death by a mad-man! It's scarcely believable, is it? — One of those things that happen to other people: never to oneself.'

I heard the Doctor hang up and then the voice of the nurse on the stairs saying: 'She's stirring, Doctor. I think you had better come.'

'Right, nurse.' Then to me from the passage: 'Come upstairs now, will you, my boy? Gently as you can, for Heaven's sake. And not a word until she has completely recognized you — understood?'

'Understood,' I replied, and followed him with a thumping heart.

In the soft pink glow of her bedside lamp, she lay on her side, lightly covered by a silken sheet. At our entrance her eyes opened drowsily. A little groan of pain escaped her.

I moved cautiously forward, thankful to see her eyes, despite the lingering effect of the sedative, slowly lighting up.

'Hubert,' her voice was weak but resonant, 'darling Hubert; why have you taken so long?'

'Mooghie, Mooghie,' I faltered, 'imagine my haste. But seven hours ago I was in far-off Lowestoft; all amongst the shrimps and winkles, where the early sea-weeds blow. I — '

She winced painfully. 'Darling, don't, don't please make me laugh. It's such Hell when I move.'

The soft arm encircling my neck was deliciously cool but I had to take care about kissing her. Her lower lip was cut and swollen and she had an appalling black eye. Yet, with brave defiance, her Italian jasmines insisted that she would soon be an epic beauty once more.

Her father, still shaken by the savage attack upon his daughter, went over to the small fire burning in a pretty wrought-iron grate, and affected to busy himself with the poker.

'You know,' she whispered, 'I woke up an hour ago and heard you coming up the drive. I could have died of joy. Darling Hubert!'

'I know. I actually felt you hearing me. I knew you were O.K. after all. I almost flopped out on the doorstep with relief.'

'Twins,' she murmured. 'Heavenly Twins. Oh, don't go away, Hubert, my angel. Please don't go away . . . !'

The Doctor approached the bed. I rose to my feet. Her eyes didn't leave my face.

'I'm going to show you.' grunted her father grimly, 'what that damned pervert has done to my daughter. Come round here and brace yourself.'

'Daddy — please don't . . . Please!' she started to cry quietly.

Gently but firming ignoring her pleas, he tenderly lifted aside the sheet.

At what he revealed, outrage and compassion choked me. I had to stifle a cry of absolute fury. From the nape of her neck to her buttocks a dozen or so livid weals disfigured the peach-bloom of her skin. Some of them had exuded blood onto the sheet of gauze dressing. Swallowing an angry sob I turned away, quite unable to endure the pitiful shaking of her shoulders. This was a hundred years from the frosty morning with the robin, the red lamps of the surviving apples in the garden, the Christmas Roses and her child's sea-blue eyes with their Magyar tilt, gazing into mine with the completest trust. Love at first sight . . . the real thing. I saw her with her offering of her dinner mince pie held out to me in her tiny pink handkerchief: her dear little pink gingham drawers. At the moment I could have gladly done Mr Pierpoint's job for him on Monkey-Man.

Her father replaced the sheet. He said: 'Now cut off, young Hubert, and jump into that bath Netta is running for you, then get your pyjamas on and come back here. You're looking about done in.'

That night I slept on a chaise-lounge beside her bed; her hand in mine. At first she slept fitfully, uttering little cries of pain and fear but a murmured word or two from me was enough to soothe her off again.

I awoke very early to find her in a profound slumber, dead to the world and breathing quietly. I had a feeling that her father might consider my further presence in her bedroom unnecessary in the circumstances, so I put on my dressing-gown and slippers and quietly left the room. Where, I wondered desperately, could I get a cup of tea at such an unearthly hour?

The next door in the passage stood half-ajar and there issued the sweet sound of tea-spoons and cups. The nurse was up and about and, on my assurance that her charge was asleep, shared with me the most delectable cup of tea that I had tasted in my life.

It was perfect, that morning. The garden was wildly beautiful in the wake of the storm. It smelt like early autumn until a hazy, then a brilliant sun drew up the gauzy vapours like a vast golden back-drop of iridescent silk, and transformed all to summer again. The lawn was spread with a carpet of fallen scarlet crab-apples, sparkling with last night's rain.

Quietly I unlatched the French doors to the verandah, drew my dressing gown around me and, rolling into the hammock, lit one of my remaining Abdullahs, drawing fumes deep into my lungs and expelling them sensuously through my nose. From the kitchen quarters came the sound of early-morning female voices. There even seemed to be a pleasant dew upon them. Then came the agreeable acridity of a kitchen stove raked out and refuelled.

At what time did the family come to the surface?

And there, as if forcing itself upon my attention, whether I would or no, from the rear of the plantation of fir-trees, the Lumie Tree rustled the golden springs of its leaves, with a certain insistence about it. Pines, orchard trees, rose-bushes, swayed scarce perceptibly, yet that infernal Lumie Tree's greeny-gold springs and plumes tossed and rustled and scintillated with an animation that was downright uncanny. I tell you: it gave me the grues up the spine. I felt my dislike of it turning to hatred. I actually began to seek among its twisted limbs a perfect one from which, with hideous convenience, Monkey-Man might have hanged himself in the confusion of remorse.

Without warning, there swept over me, on a wave of acute mental pain, a vision of the little house in All Saints Avenue, full of our furniture and our intimate possessions, but no longer our home and refuge from the rough, tough world outside it: empty, now, and silent save for the squeak and scrabble of a mouse, the rhythmic tap-tap of a blind-cord's wooden acorn against a skirting-board, the chronic dripping of the kitchen tap. Here, lapped in the felicities and luxuries of Mooghie's magnificent home, misery nearly overwhelmed me. Blissful hopes and prospects presented themselves momentarily in scary masks of alarming vagueness.

I rolled from the hammock, feeling for another cigarette, angry with myself for giving way so feebly to the effects of over-fatigue and prolonged anxiety.

I strolled to the verandah's end. Somewhere, two miles or so beyond Cliveden's highest hump, our Avenue would be all alive by now, with the daily-breaders, once so contemptible in their smug decorum, and now like fellow defenders of a beleaguered city: The City Of Childhood. Dear Mr Spindler on his portentous bicycle with the wooden goody-box strapped to the carrier, trailing the fragrant blue smoke of his silver-banded, mellow aged pipe: Messrs Goss, Hardy, Amphlet, Baker and the rest — not forgetting the grizzly Mr Heavens, longing, doubtless for Ma's return. Appleyards, Smiths and Bonds, inordinately proud of the near possession of their homes, as yet finding car-ownership well out of their reach, little knowing that such ownership would transform them one of these days from courteous, leisured pedestrians into exasperated proprietors of potentially lethal weapons. One of them had, it was of course well-known, a son with a bed-wetting problem: another a daughter like the Gorgon, madly but hoeplessly enamoured of my young brother, Victor.

Then there would be Mr Humphries, shoving his milk-cart up the steep slope of Gordon Road crying: 'MILK-HO-HO!' His churn would be gleaming brazenly, his great box-like boots booming hollowly, one before the other, at an apparently impossibly obtuse angle - like Charlie Chaplin, but infinitely funnier. Mr Williams, the greengrocer, with his mild-mannered pony and his great curly Wessex moustache; Mr Bickly, the handsome young baker's roundsman in his bouncy little G.W.K. and his fetishistic breeches; girls and boys, some of them once indifferently regarded, now intensely lovable: from crisp, muslin-sweet Betty Venables to piddley-knickered little Hickle Shrubsole and, dashing, imperiously pretty Renee, taking a short cut through our garden, vaulting the gate, leaping the flower beds and out by the back gate with its otiose warning to 'Beware of the Dog.' I hung on to the verandah railing, saying goodbye to them all, tears pricking the back of my eyes.

In retrospect I saw my father's lean, Italianate face: dejected, apprehensive of the future, yet movingly self-forgetful, and in fancy, my mother, all cock-a-hoop and jubilant at the prospect of being returned to her native heath and as certain as the sun rose in the East of regretting it within the month, and blaming the poor man for everything — if he

Dear Mr Spindler on his portentuous bicycle — here with Mrs S; dashing, imperiously pretty Renée Spindler, bosom friend, with some of her high-diving trophies; and Nancy Spindler with Mr and Mrs Woolf.

189

had not already toiled himself to death at a proprietorship he no more wanted than he was capable of sustaining.

At this point the Doctor called me into breakfast. I could hear him humming *Diane* as I went by his study. Obviously he had found Mooghie going on well. His wife was not yet down. The Lumie Tree had dismissed me with an ironical shaking of leaves: a sinister susurration, a malevolent sound reminiscent of Caliban, son of Sycorax, sniggering from within his imprisoning tree.

I set myself to gobble my kidneys and kedgeree; anxious only to get up to my love.

With pleased surprise I found her propped in a prettily curvaceous Victorian sofa, her back supported by a large air-cushion. She was now attired in a light, flowered gown and looked, despite her swollen lips and bruised face, radiant.

Her bedroom had two windows. She had chosen the one facing west in order to conceal the livid bruising of her right eye. Through the half-drawn curtains of the other window, a great beam of sunshine threw an oblique, butter-coloured strip of light over a Cerise carpet. Her bed was of attractively designed wrought iron, painted white. Instead of ordinary knobs, the posts were capped in gilt. The briskly ticking clock on the mantle was a Dresden shepherdess. Behind and beside it hung a charming water-colour drawing of Bray Church. She greeted me with an air of uncertainty but with arms outstretched.

'Darling Hubert, do I, could I, look as hideous and discouraging as I feel? Just one little kiss . . . could you possibly endure it?'

I knelt and took her face between my palms, weaving a rococo pattern of gentle kisses around and across her lovely damaged features. Then I sat back on my heels, grinning reassuringly.

'Such infinite variety,' I said. 'Even a shiner merely adorns my Mooghie!'

'Such a lovely flatterer, aren't you, love? I've got a perfectly awful feeling my lips still taste of blood and they're blown up

190

like sausages — fat ones. But thank God that poor creature spared my teeth and my nose.'

'Your lips,' I said,'taste of love and he's not a poor creature, he's a bloody louse. He ought to be castrated.'

She feigned innocence. 'What's castrated?' she inquired.

'And your back . . . Does it pain you much? I can tell you: I felt like murder when your father showed it to me last night! My word, how right old Mary Burn was about that damned loony!'

'My back, Hubert, dear? Well, there I am just a tiny bit worried. Daddy says the weals are certain to go completely, but I'm not all that cock-sure about it. Just imagine for a moment if they stayed and prevented me from wearing stage-costumes. Could you bear to appear night after night with a fubbled-up frump? It's my legs that I worry about so. I'm rather fond of them — a bit like Narcissus. When I used to see them high-kicking with the rest of the other girls it gave me one hell of a lovely kick! You know, darling, strange as it may seem, I honestly do enjoy chorus-work. It's terrifically exhilarating — at least I think so. I like the audiences better. They're — you know — ordinary down-to-earth folk . . . not élitist like the balletomanes. Do you know, Hubert, I've a feeling that I'm fundamentally common!'

'Nonsense. Common people don't use words like fundamentally.'

'No, but they enjoy dancing the Can-Can — I mean the real one. Sometimes when we did it and the band was 'specially good and we flopped down at the end, one after the other in the splits, I could have cried with excitment if we'd not all been screaming our soppy heads off.'

'Good for you!' I said. 'I nearly always enjoy a nice secret little snivel in the final movement of old Fred's *Sonata* number four. Why the hell not!'

'Old Fred . . . ?'

'Old uncle Chopin — who else? There's nobody like him. Never has been: never will be.'

'Except you, my dearest.' She kissed me more confidently. 'Darling boy.'

'Yes, my love?'

'You're not going to let me down — ever?'

'Mooghie — !'

'And you really mean to move in with us and come with me to the Varconi School?'

'Mooghie, old lady, I've burnt me boats good and proper. Here I am and here I must stay. If your parents take it into their heads to throw me out on my bot on the cold hard road, I'll have to look out for a job playing piano in some pub or other. What more can I say?'

She kissed me now in full confidence: her mouth all limp and lovely.

'I'm getting up this afternoon.' she told me. 'Daddy says it's all right and the show must go on, as they say. I'm afraid there will be a few visitors. Brenda and Phyllis Speedwell and Moira and Dennis Brierly. I can't wait to hear you playing to them.'

'Oh, God, must I?'

'Yes, my lovely, you must. Oh, yes — there's some sort of a policeman coming for to ask me some questions. You mustn't leave me. You won't, will you?'

'Supposing he insists that I do?'

'Then I button up my lip and there you are!'

A knock at the door. Netta entered with coffee and biscuits. When she had gone I moved to the window and took a look out.

'Mooghie,' I said, 'there's something extremely odd about that damn' tree of yours.'

'What tree?'

'That goddam' Lumie Tree. The leaves have all started to crinkle up since this morning. It's miles too early for a frost, yet it looks just as if they were ready to fall — and what's more they are making a noise — like as if they were giggling. Can't you hear?'

'No, sweetie, I can't — and what is more neither do I want to. Do shut up, my dear, you're giving me the creeps!'

'Oh, all right.'

'Come and get your coffee before it chills. The horrid old Lumie Tree can fall flat on its face for all I care so long as I've got you. Come on and sit down. You can put your arm round me if you like — just round my shoulder-blade part. My back's ever so much better there. Let's make the most of this morning together to plan all the lovely things we'll get up to before the School opens.'

I said: 'As far as I'm concerned I'll be perfectly happy to go on a haunt of our *Vert Paridis*. I want to see the old Park again and Grenfell Road and the Fir Walk and tthe Drive. I suppose the rhododendrons will be well over by now, but wouldn't it be nice to go to tea with Mary Burn? — and, oh yes . . . I'd like like hell to bike up to Thicket Corner one Sunday afternoon and have a glass of the Busy Bee's lemonade. He's there until the end of September with his stall. He's got a huge sort of glass tub of still lemonade with bits of the lemons floating about in it like tadpoles. The number of times I've longed for a glass on a hot Sunday evening coming home from a picnic on the Thicket. Renee always put me off, saying his glasses aren't properly washed. She said they'll give you impetigo.'

'Isn't she bossy, Renee . . . lovely but so awfully bossy? It's funny, but sometimes Brenda and I would sneak into that little sweet-shop on the corner of Hightown Road. I wonder why Miss Burn took it into her head to put it out of bounds. So tiny and innocent and shabby with one single gas-light in the window after dusk. Brenda and I would have a glass of that stuff that fizzes out of a glass ball, when the rather sweaty-looking lady in the green jersey pulls something under the counter. What's it called?'

'Vimto,' I told her. 'I used to drink pints of the stuff myself. I never caught anything from her glasses and they looked the very reverse of clean.'

'So many things to do together: nice, small silly things. I s'pose we don't really want to grow up yet. Sometimes the very idea of the theatre scares me into fits. All that travelling and new digs every week when we're on the road and new landladies and theatres and musical directors. I frighten myself just thinking about them. Sometimes I wonder if I'm really cut out for it.'

'Oh, don't!' I said. 'I feel just like that my self. We must just pull ourselves together and make up our minds to look after each other when the time comes. In the meantime let's be as frivolous and pleasure-loving as we can possibly be.'

'For a start you can row me up to Odney and I can watch you swim.'

'You can swim with me, can't you?'

'Swim! . . . with my back like it is?'

'A bit of sun on your back will work like a charm. Why, once old Juggins whopped me across my bum. Three frightful cuts! They came up like a trio of vipers. You never saw such a sight! And oozing. My dear, they'd vanished in a couple of weeks — just as yours will.'

'Oh, I do hope and pray they will. Here, I'll tell you what! We'll do something terrifically sophisticated. We'll get on the train and have tea at the Ritz! How about that!'

'The Ritz? Why I haven't the wherewithal to take you to tea at Gironimo's!'

'Darling, I've got two hundred pounds in my savings bank. We'll blow the lot on two heavenly weeks before School starts. We'll paint the Town scarlet; we'll commit every sort of unimaginable folly — we'll — '

We gave a sudden simultaneous jump. Our eyes met in startled wonder mixed with apprehension. From outside something had let loose a weird, snarling groan. It resembled the last cry of a stricken beast and was followed by the loud thrashing and crackling of smashed and broken twigs and branches, the rending of timbers, an almighty splash and churning. Then came a flooding of intensified light into the room, an enchanced brilliance of everything it contained. From the lawn arose a clamour of excited voices. Gently I removed my arm and returned to the window. Barbara was there with Netta and the cook and the gardener and his boy. Barbara looked up, saw me and gestured in a dumb-show of amazed demonstration. I returned her wave and turned back to Mooghie and the lightened room. She staggered over and tumbled into my arms, pale and a little bit shaken.

'It's the Lumie Tree,' I said. 'It's dashed well disappeared!'

And so it had. Its roots exposed by yesterday's furious down-pour and further loosened by the high wind, it had simply walked down the muddy bank, tripped over a broken stump below, and fallen, breaking its back, into the mere, and now was invisible behind the plantation of mixed conifers. A few of its last leaves still drifted in the quiet air. Barbara was making her way over the lawn, followed by her little retinue, to survey the damage.

I looked at Mooghie to see how the happening had affected her and was immensely relieved to see a look of enchantment on her face.

A miracle had indeed taken place. That golden tree had, in its fall, disclosed a fragment of landscape as colourfully luminescent as a miniature in a monkish manuscript or book of hours.

What our eyes gazed on in something like ecstasy was a distant area of rising ground: remote, dream-like and ideal; crowned at the skyline by a row of Scots firs, joined by their foliage into the semblance of a graceful arcade. Rising to meet it, the partly carted wheat-stooks, having successfully resisted the wind and the rain, presented themselves, like grateful soldiers at ease, to the sun's now high and flaming rays, and quivered in the heat-haze. The stubble seemed to be moving softly as a summer ocean, as passing cloud-shadows wrought their aerial magic and, as we gazed, bewitched by this marvellous transformation-scene, tiny, toy-like, a farm-waggon, drawn by a pair of shire-horses, came into view, plodding behind the firs, passing them slowly, one by one, the copper ornaments hanging from the horses' necks emitting an occasional flash and gleam of brightness.

A sudden surge of intense joy ran through my veins, a flood of intoxicating satisfaction. This abruptly revealed prospect had awakened within me a sense of having within my view almost within my grasp - a glorious abstraction, a sweet summary of my entire life lived to date upon the three magic miles of the Bath Road: from Robert Taylor's handsome bridge — for me the archetype of all bridges — by Bridge

Street and the gypsy-haunted Moor; through the individualistic, cheerful animation of High Street with its family shops and its characteristic scents, smells and — yes — its stinks; up Castle Hill past the realms of Miss Burn and Miss Mayne and all the doctors in their Terrace opposite Castle House; along by the domiciliary symbols of the splendid Victorian success-story; across All Saints Avenue with its treasure-hoard of personal memories and on down Punt Hill, where Mrs Egbert had suffered her encounter with Canon Drummond's apparition; leaving on the left the sombre umbragiousness of Dick Turpin's Lane and our old rust-scabbed pump and it's putative voice ('Stap me, Dick! Gadzooks, sirrah! Zounds!) until the harsh sweetness of bracken hit the nostrils, the little narrow paths opened before you, leading to the sudden hush and honey-suckle fragrance, the wood-pigeons enhancement of silence and, from April to July, the spell-binding, bland resonance of the cuckoo's shouting, to the Thicket: the never-ploughed, secretive, lover-frequented Thicket surrounding you with lofty trees, shadow-dappled turf, impenetrably thorned sloe-bushes and briars and its celestial atmosphere of primeval tranquillity.

Simultaneously we withdrew our eyes from the new panorama, regarding each other with entranced wonder.

'That field,' said Mooghie softly, 'is called Granny's Grave. How often we've walked there; but it's never looked like this before. So tiny and perfect — like a little bit of Paradise on earth. I say a jolly good riddance to the Lumie Tree. Daddy should have had it chopped down years ago!'

Earlier that morning, the gardener had cleared a circular bed of faded tobacco-plants and heliotrope. The warm breeze wafted the rich scent of freshly-turned earth and pulled roots up to us at the window.

From a mulberry tree darted, quick as a flash of light, in one sudden swoop, a small robin: young, warm-brown, as yet unadorned with his scarlet badge of manhood. Dapper, stiffly erect, he perched upon the gardener's abandoned spade, shrilled a brilliant roulade of notes, paused and gave the hop of a cheeky little urchin.

'My goodness!' gasped Mooghie, 'isn't it all lovely?'

END

The Thames at Maidenhead: isn't it all lovely?

Acknowledgements

The pictures and map in this book have all been taken from the author's personal collection, and that of his editor, with the exception of three items kindly lent by the Berkshire County Library, Maidenhead Branch. For picture research, the author is indebted to Mrs Pat Curtis and Mr Julian Dunn for seeking out late Edwardian and 1920s material specific to this story, set as it is in a period with few surviving visual records which are readily available. Copies of the author's and editor's pictures are being deposited with the Maidenhead Library.

List of Illustrations

Subscribers
Presentation Copies

1 The Royal Borough of Windsor and Maidenhead
2 Berkshire County Council
3 Maidenhead Library

4 Stanley Woolf
5 Clive & Carolyn Birch
6 Sue Halliday
7 Julie Palmer
8 Rose Minshull
9 Mark & Joan Heavens
10 K. J. Fry
11 E. W. Fry
12 Mrs B.P. Woodley
13 Pat & Derek Taylor
14 D. Young
15 Mrs P. Venner
16 Miss Kim E. Willis
17 Graham Carter
18 Fiona Millward
19 Judith & Nigel Millward
20 Miss Delia Radley
21 Miss J. Edmonds
22 Mrs Avis J. Harvey
23 Mrs B. H. McQueen
24 Mrs J. Foster-Key
25 Marten Collins
26 Mrs L.M.G. Williams
27 T. Deadman
28 Mrs S.A. Stannett
29 Mrs J.A. Smart
30 Dennis D. Dormer
31 Cherine Collins
32 Miss Isabella I Spriggs
33 Miss P.J. Matthews
34 J. Howorth
35 Bill & Peggy Butler
36 Mrs A. Jinman
37 E. Sammes
38 Mrs Sheila A. Groves
39 Roy Bates
40 Maurice & Doris Eggett
41 Mrs Edwards

42 Mrs M.A. Martin
43 B.L. Mackroy
44 Kenneth E. Bodenham
45 Alan Badcock
46 Mrs M. Chamberlain
47 Joan Cooper
48 Mrs M. Wright
49 Robert D. Brown
50 Anne Atkinson
51 Mrs M. E. Wilkey
52 Raymond White
53 Mrs Jeanne Blake
54 Sydney E. Fisher
55 Mrs E. J. Smart
56 Jane & Donald Lockyer
57 W. R. Compton
58 Ronald Blythe
59 Betty Harvey
60 A. Prothero
61 Florence Rickerby
62
63 Mrs E. N. Dunnett
64 Dr Roger Sauvan-Smith
65 Mrs V. Brock
66 R. Sparks
67 Jean Stockings
68 Mrs D. E. Bonnyman
69 Roger Vaughan
70 Margaret & Mary Biggs
71
72 M. L. Aylmer
73
74 Mrs A. M. Marriott
75
76 Jeremy Woolf
77 David Jefferson
78
82 Erika Seekings

199

83 Sydney A. Stone
84 Mrs I. V. Smith
85
87 Margaret Anne Hawthorn
88 Henry Thomas & Mrs Maisie Ruth Willard
89 N. D. Brandon-King
90 Michael & Helen Perry
91 Leslie John Woodbridge
92 James F. Eves
93 Mrs M. J. Moss
94
95 R. Lacey
96 Mr & Mrs D. S. Good
97 Gerald F. Gammon
98 John R. H. Neve JP
99 O. J. Miles
100 W. E. Knight
101 Mrs E. M. West
102 Mr & Mrs Tom Middleton
103 Phyllis Piddington
104 Nationwide Anglia Building Society
105 B. White
106 V. J. A. Kemp
107 Ronald Vaughan
108 K. W. Lovett
109 Mr & Mrs G. Aldridge
110 Michael Wilson
111 Mrs R. Dunnett (née Spindler)
112 A. F. White
113 Mrs A. Robinson
114 Richard Barnes
115 Simon Aylmer
116 James F. Eves
117
120 Mrs Doreen Cazzini
121
122 Miss Dorothy Smith
123 Harry Roy Horsham
124 Geoffrey Peter Bennett
125 C. A. R. Cutler
126 Miss M. Young

127 B. L. Mackrory
128 S. H. & M. E. Plank
129 Suzanne Webb
130 Jill Woodward
131 Carole Selway
132 Holyport CE Primary School
133 Mr & Mrs T. White
134 Pamela Knight
135 James William Webb
136 Mrs J. R. Mundy
137 Ann G. Hay
138 Alec Davidson
139 Mrs A. Whitehead
140 Mrs Patricia C. Moore
141 Mrs P. P. Rafter
142 Richard L. Chamberlain
143 Philip E. J. Scotcher
144 E. W. L. Pike
145 Derek R. Eales
146 Jean Hazell
147 James L. Calder
148 Elizabeth M. King
149 Carole Rennie
150 Mrs Myrtle Davis
151 Mrs Barbara Elsey
152 Mr & Mrs R. M. Burdett
153 Lina & Mike Cole
154 Stanley Thomas Harmsworth
155 George Littleton
156 Brian White
157 Miss C. Butcher
158
159 Valerie Fenwick
160 J. A. Sloan & Family
161
162 B. R. Eastick
163 Irene Edna Baldwin
164
168 Maidenhead Library
169 Berkshire County Library
170 Mrs J. Tildesley

Remaining names unlisted

200